0500000834932 1

CAMDEN COUNTY LIBRARY
203 LAUREL ROAD
VOORHEES, NJ 08043

SEP 1 4 2017

CAMDEN COUNTY LIBRARY
203 LAUREL ROAD
VOORHEES, NJ 08043

SEP 1 4 2017

Dengeki Daisy

Vol. 13

Story & Art by
Kyousuke Motomi

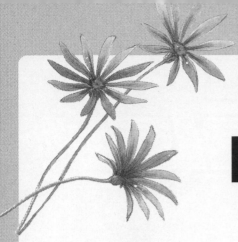

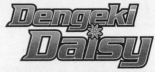

Volume 13
CONTENTS

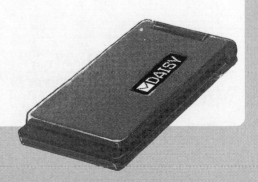

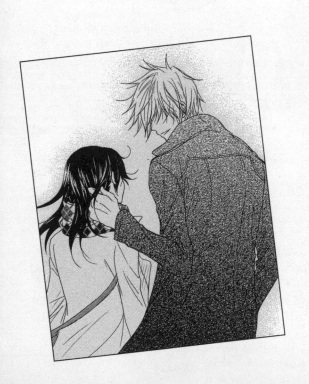

Dengeki Daisy Vol. 13

★ **Tasuku Kurosaki** ★
Continues to protect Teru as "Daisy." "Daisy" is his handle from his days as a hacker. He is in love with Teru.

★ **Teru Kurebayashi** ★
Although she is poor and has no living relatives, Teru remains positive and true to herself. A second-year high school student, she has deep feelings for Kurosaki.

★ Teru discovers that Kurosaki is Daisy, the mysterious person who supported and encouraged her after her brother Soichiro's death. Thinking that there must be a reason why Kurosaki has chosen to hide his identity, Teru decides to keep this knowledge to herself.

★ During this time, Teru's life is threatened, and strange incidents involving Teru and Kurosaki occur. Kurosaki decides to disclose the truth to Teru, but Akira beats him to it and tells her about Kurosaki's past "sin." Learning what Akira has done, Kurosaki disappears from sight. Seeing Teru so despondent, the Director and Riko tell her about Kurosaki's past.

★ Teru learns that Kurosaki's father was involved with the development of a top-secret government code, and his death was shrouded in mystery. Kurosaki became a hacker to clear his father's

CHARACTERS...

★ Akira ★
Chiharu Mori's partner-in-crime. He continues to stalk Teru and Kurosaki.

★ Takeda ★
Soichiro's former coworker. He is the owner of Kaoruko, a Shiba dog.

★ Boss (Masuda) ★
Currently runs the snack shop "Flower Garden" but used to work with Soichiro.

★ Soichiro Kurebayashi ★
Teru's older brother and a genius systems engineer. He died after leaving Teru in Kurosaki's care.

★ Chiharu Mori ★
She used to work at Teru's school. Teaming up with Akira, she continues to target Teru and Kurosaki.

★ Antler ★
He tricked Kurosaki into creating the "Jack Frost" virus.

★ Director (Kazumasa Ando) ★
He used to work with Soichiro and is currently the director of Teru's school.

★ Riko Onizuka ★
She was Soichiro's girlfriend and is now a counselor at Teru's school.

STORY...

name and created the code virus known as "Jack Frost." In order to save Kurosaki from being charged with a "Jack Frost"-related murder, Soichiro worked nonstop to decipher the code and died in the process. Teru accepts this newfound knowledge about Kurosaki. She thanks him for all that he has done for her and asks him to stay by her side.

★ Teru and company foil a plot that was going to use a new version of the "Jack Frost" virus for foul purposes. Working together strengthens the bond between Teru and Kurosaki, but Kurosaki then gets a call from Antler! Antler sends them the key to M's Last Testament and throws everyone into confusion. Meanwhile, Akira escapes from Chiharu's clutches, but where is he headed...?!

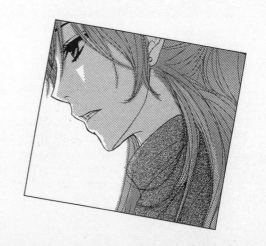

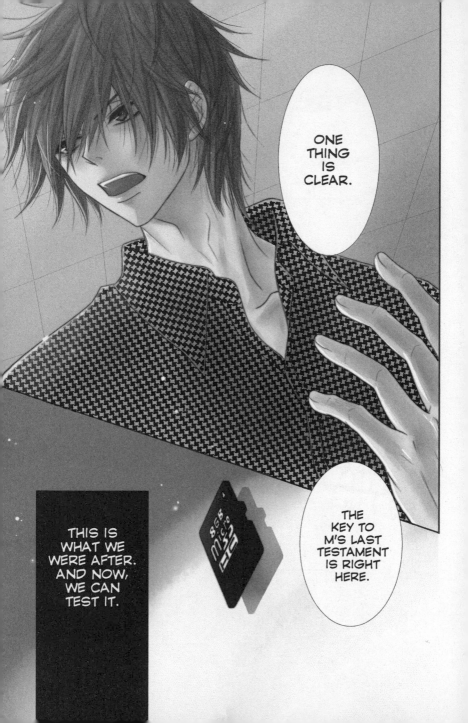

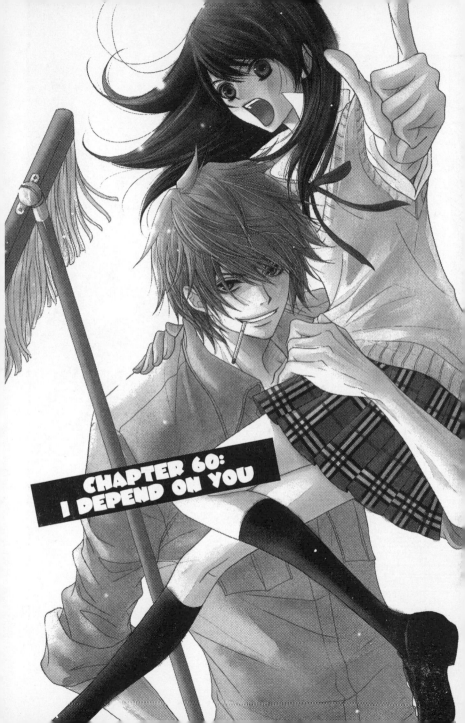

CHAPTER 60:
I DEPEND ON YOU

HELLO, EVERYONE!! IT'S KYOUSUKE MOTOMI.
DENGEKI DAISY IS AT VOLUME TH–THIRTEEN!!!
ALREADY…13. THIRTEEN.
LIKE A TEENAGER. OR A SUIT IN A DECK
OF CARDS.

OR THAT FRIDAY. …AS ALWAYS,
I'M HOVERING BETWEEN HAPPY
EXCITEMENT AND EXHAUSTION FROM
LACK OF SLEEP. BUT ANYWAY, I MADE IT.
THANK YOU SO MUCH.

I'D BE REALLY PLEASED IF YOU ENJOYED THIS
ONE EVEN A LITTLE BIT TOO!!

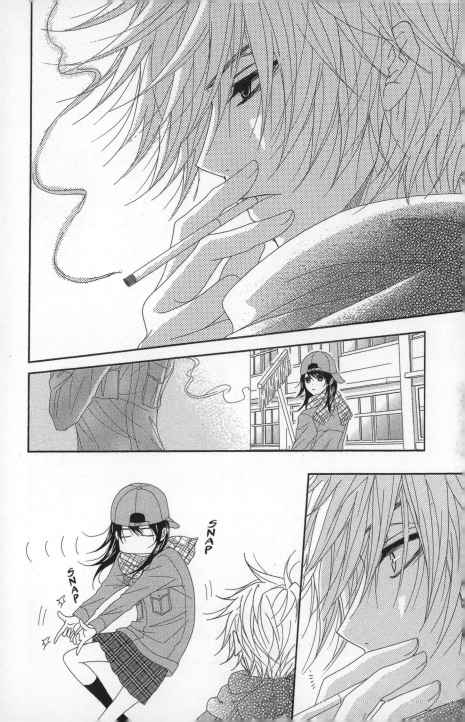

OKAY, OKAY.

SORRY, FOR WHATEVER I DID.

SHEESH! IT TOOK YOU LONG ENOUGH TO NOTICE MY SEXY DANCE.

WHEN SOMEONE CALLS, ANSWER. DON'T JUST ZONE OUT.

I was about to flash my belly button.

Sexy dance...?

SORRY, I WAS THINKING.

HA HA... I'LL BET. BUT DON'T LET IT BOTHER YOU.

I CAN GUESS ABOUT WHAT...

IT'S NOT LIKE WE'RE IN A BIND.

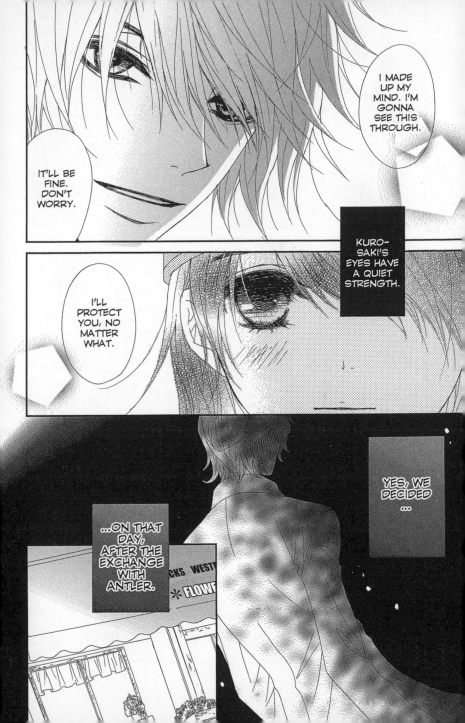

HE HAD SENT US M'S LAST TESTAMENT...

YES. THERE ARE RISKS. IT COULD BE DANGEROUS.

AND STICK OUR NECK'S OUT WHILE SEARCHING FOR M'S LAST TESTAMENT?

WE SHOULD MOVE QUICKLY IF WE DON'T WANT THIS FALLING INTO THE WRONG HANDS.

THAT MEANS THERE ARE OTHER INTERESTED PARTIES.

ANTLER ASKED, "WHO WILL OPEN THE PANDORA'S BOX?"

I THINK WE SHOULD TRY TO DECIPHER...

M'S LAST TESTAMENT...

...WAS LEFT BY OUR MENTOR, THE LATE PROFESSOR MIDORIKAWA, SO...

WE DON'T KNOW HOW MANY, OR IF ANYONE ELSE GOT THIS KEY.

...THIS KEY OURSELVES.

...I COULD NEVER FORGIVE MYSELF IF I JUST LOOKED THE OTHER WAY.

GRP

NOT AFTER THE PROFESSOR AND SOICHIRO AND OTHERS DIED FOR THIS.

I WANT TO PROVE HIM WRONG. BESIDES...

HE THINKS WE CHERISH OUR LIVES TOO MUCH TO GET INVOLVED.

I AGREE WITH ANDY.

ANTLER SHOWED HIS HAND BECAUSE HE DOESN'T THINK MUCH OF US.

IF ENDURING THE SADNESS AND SUPPRESSING OUR FEELINGS FOR OUR FRIENDS...

...WEAKENS US AS A TEAM, THEN WE'VE GOT OUR PRIORITIES BACKWARDS.

RIGHT NOW, WE'RE ALL IN THE SAME PLACE EMOTIONALLY.

RIGHT?

I'M SORRY, I'M LETTING MY EMOTIONS RULE.

FORGET WHAT I—

NO, YOU'RE RIGHT.

16

I SAY WE CARRY ON FOR THEM AND FIND M'S LAST TESTAMENT.

PROFESSOR MIDORIKAWA AND SOICHIRO DIED TRYING TO TELL US SOMETHING.

YEAH...

YAK

WE DON'T NEED YOU TO TELL US.

That means you two.

THINGS'LL PROBABLY GET CRAPPY, SO BE READY.

YAK

YAK

AND WE GOTTA GET ALONG. REMEMBER, TEAMWORK.

LET'S SUCK IT UP AND DO THIS.

DON'T APOLOGIZE. I WANNA HELP TOO.

Still, thank you.

TERU... I'M SORRY WE GOT YOU INVOLVED...

I'll start by making fresh tea.

That's about it for now.

WE'LL NEED A SUPER-COMPUTER.

THEIR DECISION CAME SO NATURALLY.

IT SHOWED THE DEPTH OF THEIR DEVOTION AND THE URGENCY THEY FELT.

Thank you, Teru.

GETTING ONE WON'T BE EASY.

FIRST, WE HAVE TO DECIPHER THE KEY.

THESE KIND ADULTS HAD QUIETLY SHOULDERED THEIR ANGUISH...

But we could ask a certain agency, right, Boss?

I COULDN'T BEGIN TO IMAGINE THE WEIGHT OF THEIR REMORSE.

Probably... Once I give them the details.

SO WHO WAS I...

...TO OPPOSE THE PATH THEY CHOSE?

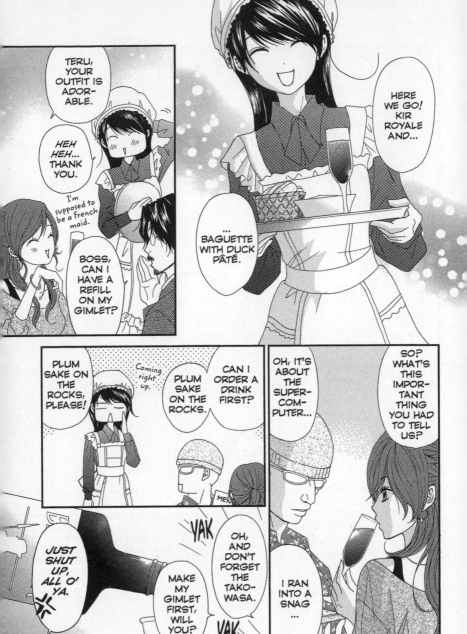

FLOWER GARDEN IS UNDER RENOVATION, AND WE HAVE TO THINK ABOUT SECURITY.

GRRR

I TAUGHT YOU HOW TO MIX DRINKS LONG AGO, SO HANG IN THERE, BOSS.

At least I brought the food.

BOSS, DON'T CALL ME "BOSS." IT'S CONFUSING!!!

God, mixing drinks is a pain in the ass

FLOWER GARDEN HAS MOVED HERE (TEMPORARILY)

(TEMPORARY) BARTENDER

THIS IS *MY* PLACE, YOU KNOW. DAMMIT!

WHY AM I DOING THIS ANYWAY? THIS IS CRAZY!!

NO. A LOT OF GUYS FEEL THE SAME WAY WE DO ABOUT M'S LAST TESTAMENT.

THEY'RE MORE THAN HAPPY TO HELP, EXCEPT THEIR SUPER-COMP IS BEING USED.

SHK

SHK

ANYWAY, WHAT WERE YOU SAYING?

ABOUT THE SUPER-COMPUTER... DID THE AGENCY TURN YOU DOWN?

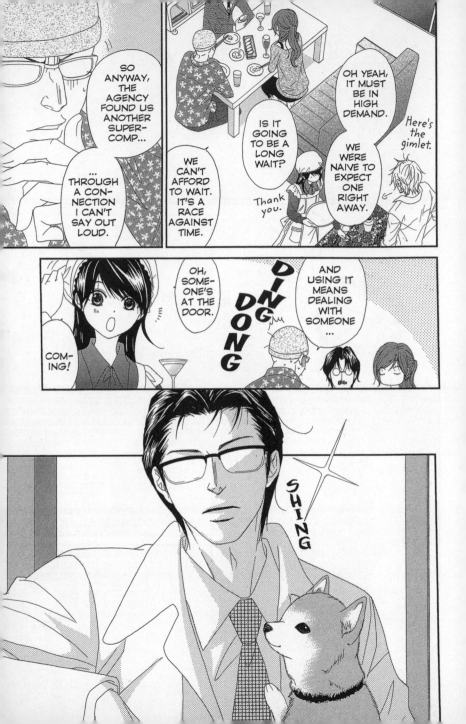

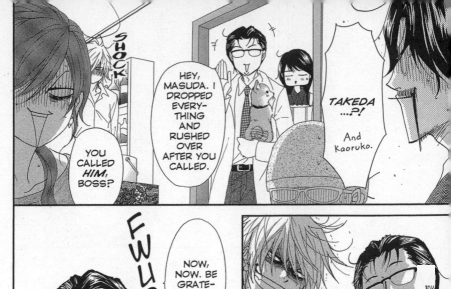
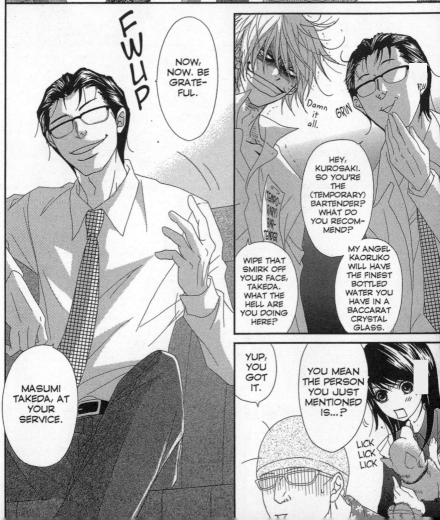

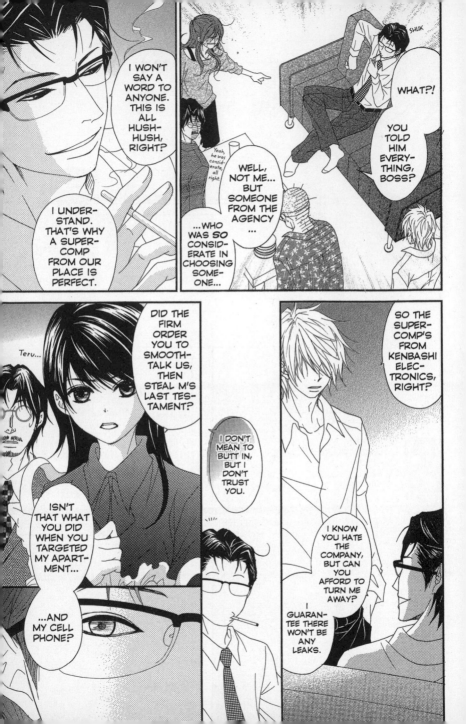

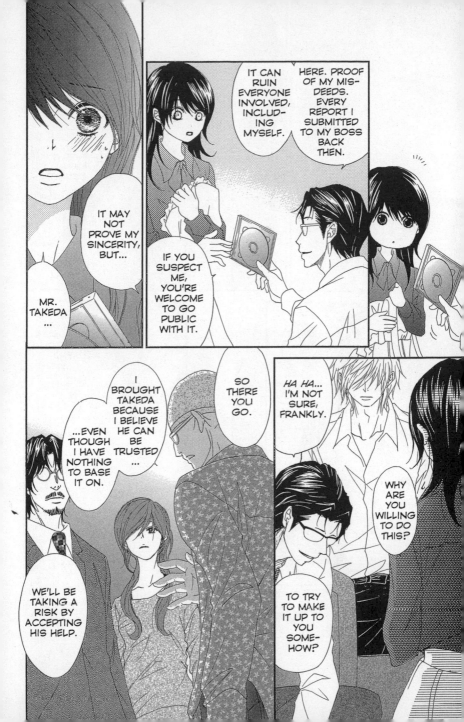

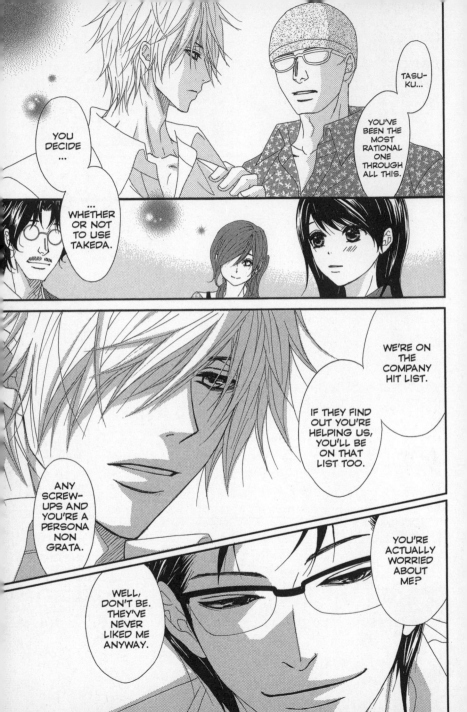

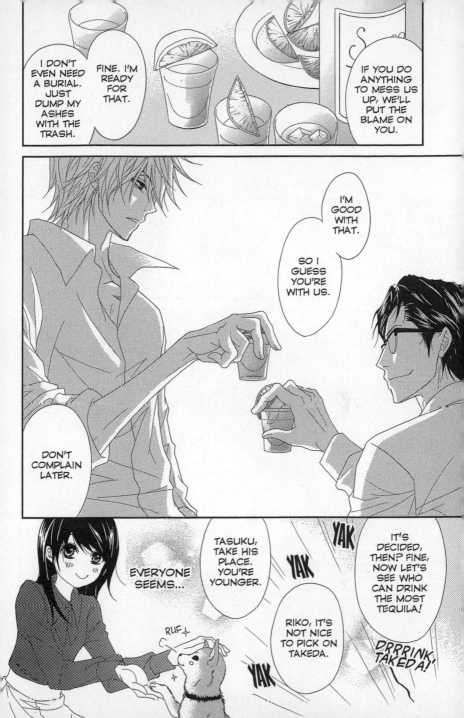

...AND AT PEACE...

...SO RELAXED...

...EVEN THOUGH THEY'RE ABOUT TO CONFRONT SOMETHING REALLY BIG...

HEY, CUT IT OUT.

LICK LICK

MY EARS... ARE REALLY TICKLISH...

MMM...

WHAT IS IT?

MMMM...

WHAT, TERU? YOU'RE COMING ON SO STRONG...

I DON'T MIND IF YOU WANT TO...

BUT IF RIKO FINDS OUT, SHE'LL KILL...

OH, KURO-SAKI. ARE YOU UP?

WHOOSH

I WAS JUST DREAMING. IT'S THIS MUTT'S FAULT...

ACTUALLY, I'M A JERK. I'LL SLIT MY BELLY. I'LL GO BALD TOMOR-ROW!

PEEK

Don't bother cleaning up.

Sorry. I'm going to take these two home.

EVERYONE LEFT WHILE YOU WERE ASLEEP.

BOSS WAS THE ONLY ONE WHO WAS SOBER.

Sorry, Teru. I'm going home to throw up in my own bathroom.

OH... YEAH. OKAY.

ALL THE ADULTS GOT PRETTY DRUNK.

IT'S OKAY. I'M NOT UPSET THAT YOU PASSED OUT.

Ah ha ha...

Ah ha ha...

You must cherish your hair.

TH-THMP
TH-THMP

NATURALLY, SHE DIDN'T GET IT.

LICK LICK

I'M KEEPING KAORUKO FOR THE NIGHT.

MR. TAKEDA WAS OUT OF IT TOO, SO I'LL TAKE HER BACK TOMOR-ROW.

HEH HEH...

YOU'RE STILL DRUNK.

NO WAY. I DIDN'T PUT THAT MUCH ALCOHOL IN MY DRINK. Besides, I fell asleep.

MM-MM, KURO-SAKI...

MAYBE WE SHOULDA BEEN NICER TO TAKEDA...

FORCING DRINKS ON HIM AND NOT BOTHER-ING TO SAY THANKS...

WE'RE EXPECT-ING A LOT OUTTA HIM.

WHEN YOU'RE DRUNK, YOU'RE SORT OF CHILD-LIKE...

THERE'S AN HONESTY ABOUT YOU THAT'S CUTE.

ELEMENTARY SCHOOL STUDENT ↓

POUT

OH, I EMBAR-RASSED YOU.

I'M NOT EMBAR-RASSED! NO WAY! NUH-UH!

THAT'S STUPID! LEARN TO RESPECT YOUR ELDERS!

Oh ho ho ho ho

HERE'S SOME MILK.

for dogs.

COME, KAO-RUKO.

PERK

!!

SHUP

NO THANKS. I HAVE OOLONG TEA.

WANT ME TO GET SOME WATER FOR YOU?

CHUCKLE

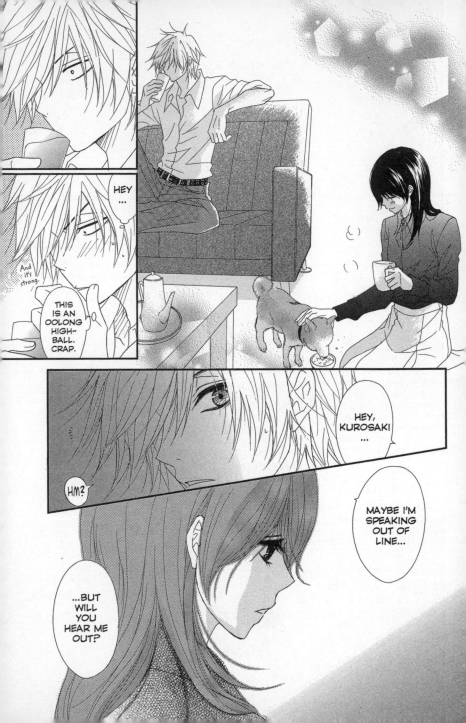

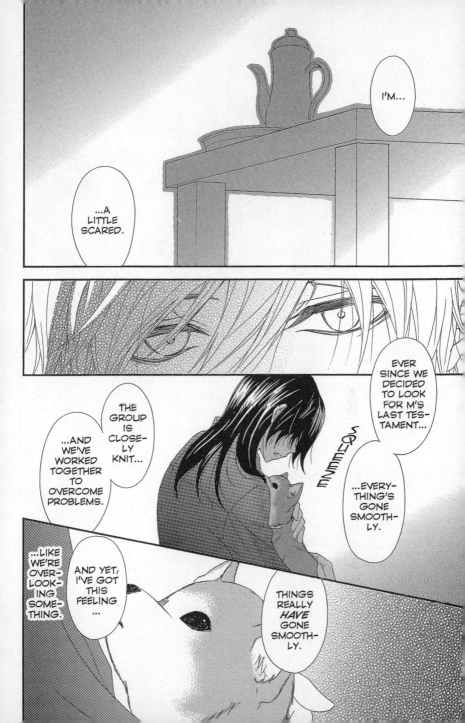

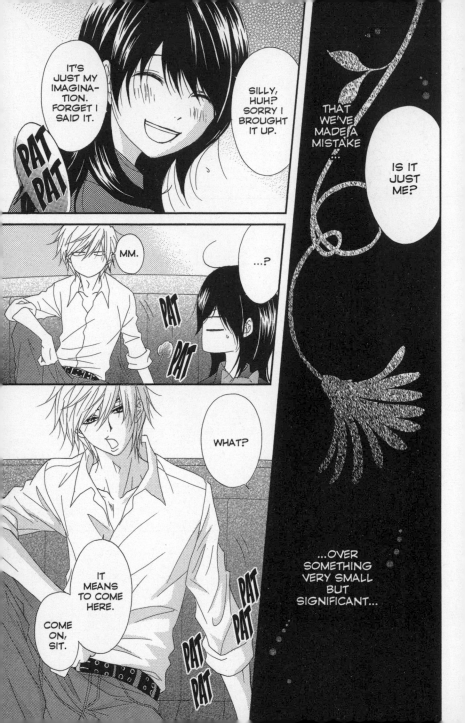

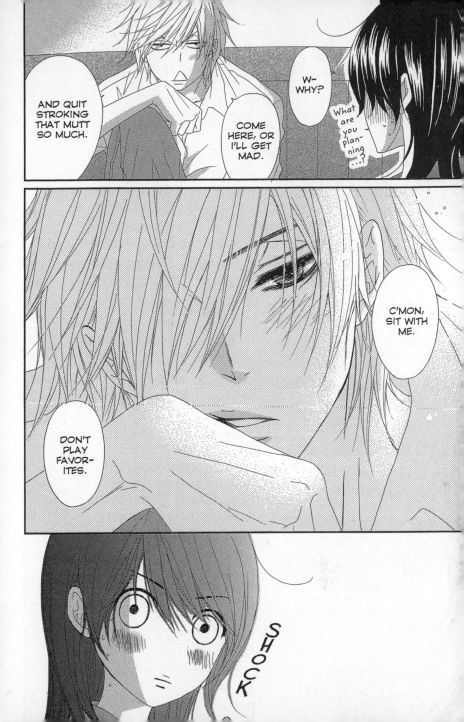

WELL, THIS WAS A MISTAKE.

IF YOU'RE NOT DRUNK, THEN YOU'RE A PERVERT. GETTING JEALOUS OVER A DOG...

I'M NOT JEAL-OUS.

WHAT? I'M NOT DRUNK.

YOU'RE DRUNK, KURO-SAKI.

KRUNCH

KRUNCH

KRUNCH

SNACK BONE (TAKEDA BROUGHT IT.)

...

THAT'S CONVEN-IENT, BEING FORGETFUL WHEN YOU'RE DRUNK.

DID YOU FORGET ALREADY? OR ARE YOU PLAYING DUMB?

LIAR. YOU JUST SAID, "DON'T PLAY FAVOR-ITES."

WHEN I TOLD YOU TO IGNORE WHAT I SAID...

STROKE

YOU PROBABLY DON'T EVEN REMEMBER WHAT I SAID EARLIER.

I'LL BET YOU WEREN'T EVEN LIS-TENING. OH, JUST GO BALD, KURO-SAKI.

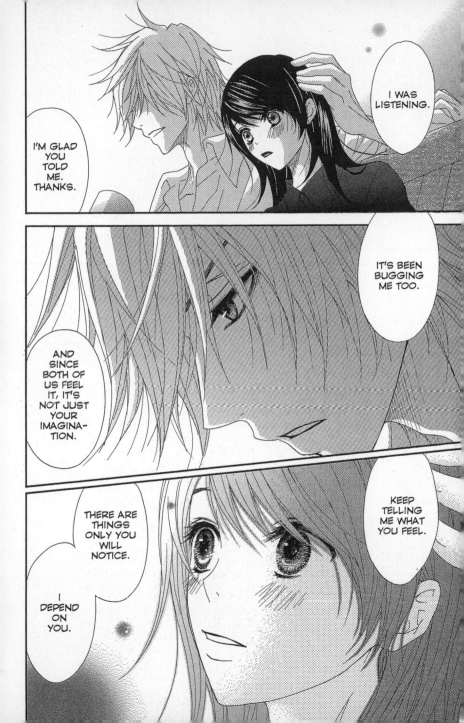

Y-YOU'RE NOT DRUNK AT ALL, KURO-SAKI.

EH HEH...

OKAY. HEH HEH...

I HAD YOU TOTALLY WRONG.

I *AM* DRUNK.

HMM... BUT WHAT WAS THAT EARLIER ABOUT NOT PLAYING FAVORITES?

TUP

TOTALLY INEBRIATED.

THAT'S WHY I CAN BE HONEST ABOUT MY FEELINGS.

IT'S REALLY WEIRD.

NO MATTER HOW WORRIED OR UNSURE I AM...

...WHEN I'M WITH YOU, I FEEL LIKE IT'LL ALL WORK OUT.

I'M GLAD KAO-RUKO'S HERE.

IF WE WERE ALONE...

...I WOULDN'T BE ABLE TO CONTROL MY...

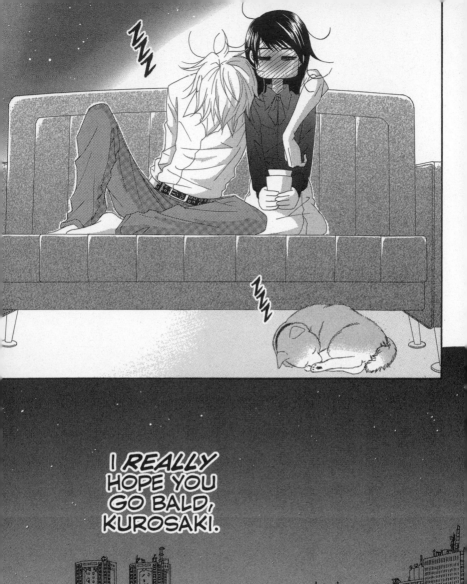

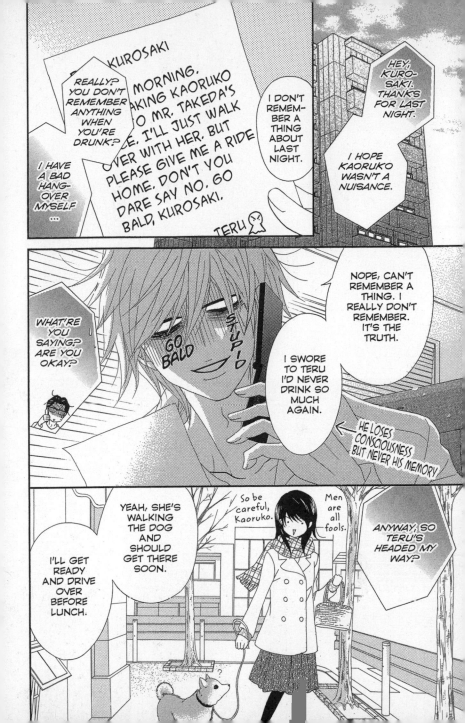

HUH? IS THAT HIM AGAIN ...?

SNAP

RINNG

RINNG

Incoming
Beware Buxom
Women

HELLO, DAISY?

LISTEN TO ME. IT'S AN EMERGENCY.

GOD, CHIHARU, DON'T TELL ME YOU'RE STILL ALIVE.

FORGET IT. I TOLD YOU NEVER TO CALL AGAIN.

WAIT!!!

IF SO, TELL HIM TO DROP DEAD.

IS THAT BASTARD AKIRA STILL AROUND?

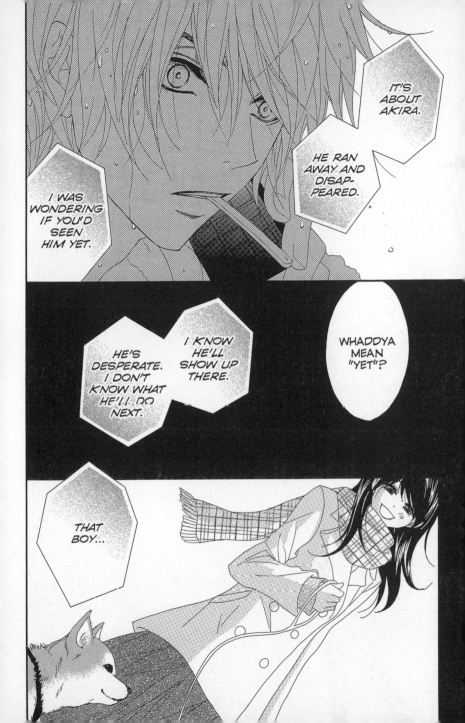

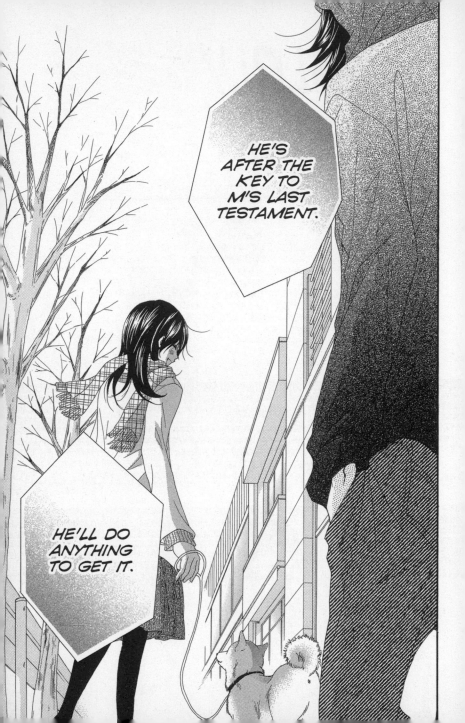

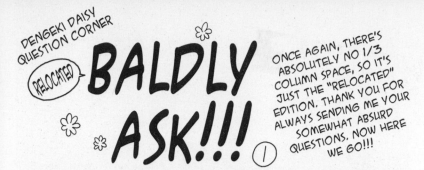

DENGEKI DAISY QUESTION CORNER

(RELOCATED) **BALDLY ASK!!!** ①

ONCE AGAIN, THERE'S ABSOLUTELY NO 1/3 COLUMN SPACE, SO IT'S JUST THE "RELOCATED" EDITION. THANK YOU FOR ALWAYS SENDING ME YOUR SOMEWHAT ABSURD QUESTIONS. NOW HERE WE GO!!!

[IN THE JAPANESE EDITION] WHY IS THE FURIGANA BY KUROSAKI'S NAME THE ONLY ONE IN KATAKANA? (I'VE BEEN WONDERING FOR QUITE SOME TIME.)

(DAISYSHIKKU@KRT, KANAGAWA PREFECTURE)

I'M SORRY, BUT THERE'S ABSOLUTELY NO SIGNIFICANCE. WHEN THE STORY WAS SERIALIZED FOR THE FIRST TIME, I WAS WORKING ON THE DIALOGUE, AND I HAVE SUCH TERRIBLE HANDWRITING THAT THE HIRAGANA LOOKED LIKE "SHIROCHIKI" RATHER THAN "KUROSAKI." SO TO MAKE SURE IT WAS READ CORRECTLY, I WROTE HIS NAME IN KATAKANA. OFTENTIMES, THINGS LIKE THAT ARE CAUGHT AND CHANGED DURING THE EDITING STAGE (FOR EXAMPLE, "探す"[SAGASU: TO SEARCH FOR SOMETHING DESIRED OR NEEDED] BECOMES "捜す"[SAGASU: TO SEARCH FOR SOMETHING LOST]). THAT'S WHAT I THOUGHT WOULD HAPPEN, BUT TO MY SURPRISE, IT WAS LEFT AS IS. I THOUGHT IT SUITED THIS GOING-THROUGH-PUBERTY HERO, SO I'VE CONTINUED TO USE IT.

AMONG THE DISHES THAT TERU PREPARES, WHAT IS KUROSAKI'S FAVORITE?

(A.N., TOKYO)

AS YOU MAY HAVE NOTICED, KUROSAKI HAS VERY CHILDLIKE TASTES. HE LIKES FOOD SERVED ON A SINGLE PLATE, LIKE HAMBURGER, OMELET WITH RICE, AND CURRY. TERU, ON THE OTHER HAND, LIKES JAPANESE CUISINE. WHEN SHE SERVES BRAISED FISH, SHE LOVES IT WHEN ONE CAREFULLY REMOVES THE BONES BEFORE EATING. KUROSAKI, WHO'S NOT VERY ADEPT AT USING CHOPSTICKS, IS CRYING INSIDE AS HE TACKLES HIS MEAL.

SOICHIRO WAS VERY GOOD AT USING CHOPSTICKS. I THINK KUROSAKI WAS INSPIRED WATCHING HIM, SO HE PRACTICED A LOT.

USING CHOPSTICKS SKILLFULLY CAN BE A VERY IMPORTANT QUALITY TO HAVE WHEN DATING.

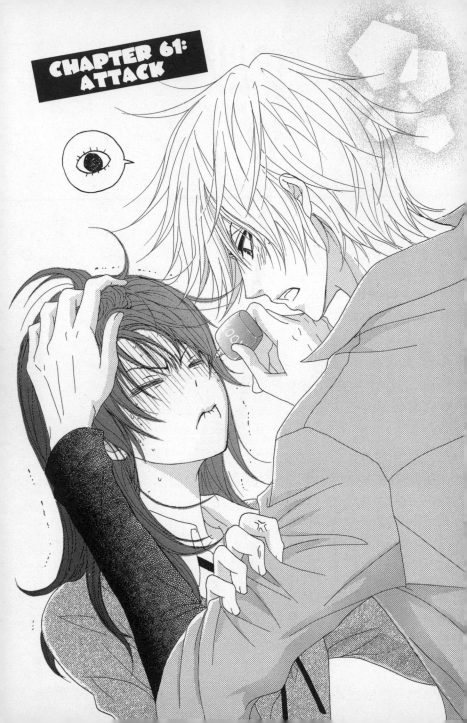

CHAPTER 61: ATTACK

I SAID HE DISAPPEARED!

HUH? WHAT DID YOU JUST SAY, CHIHARU?

HE RAN AWAY FROM ME.

WHAT ABOUT AKIRA?

WHEN HE WAS DAISY, HE WAS SO CAREFUL NOT TO LET TERU SEE WHO WAS CALLING HIS CELL PHONE. LATELY, HE'S INTO A RELATIONSHIP WHERE IT'S OKAY FOR HER TO LOOK AT HIS PHONE.

OH, WHO IS IT?

KUROSAKI, YOUR PHONE'S RINGING.

THE REASON KUROSAKI HAS CHIHARU'S NAME AS "BEWARE BUXOM WOMEN" IN HIS CELL PHONE IS... IT'S PROBABLY TO PREVENT ANY MISUNDERSTANDING WITH TERU IF CHIHARU SHOULD CALL. TERU MIGHT JUMP TO CONCLUSIONS THAT THEY WERE INVOLVED SOMEHOW, AND THINGS COULD GET UNCOMFORTABLE. KUROSAKI'S OVERTHINKING THIS. ACTUALLY, IF TERU SAW "BEWARE BUXOM WOMEN," IT'D PROBABLY GET MORE COMPLICATED WITH POINTED QUESTIONING FROM TERU.

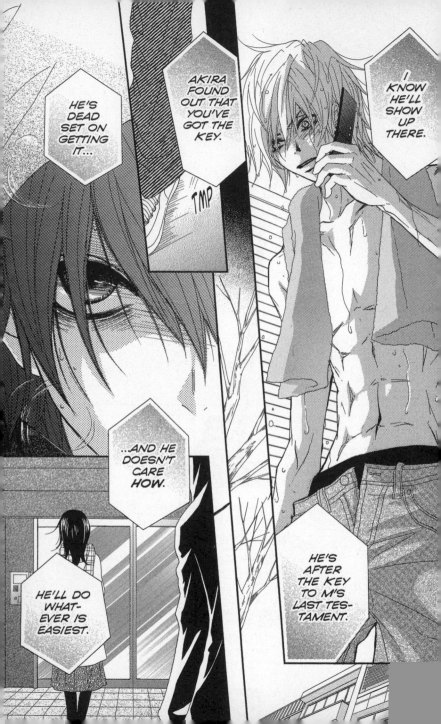

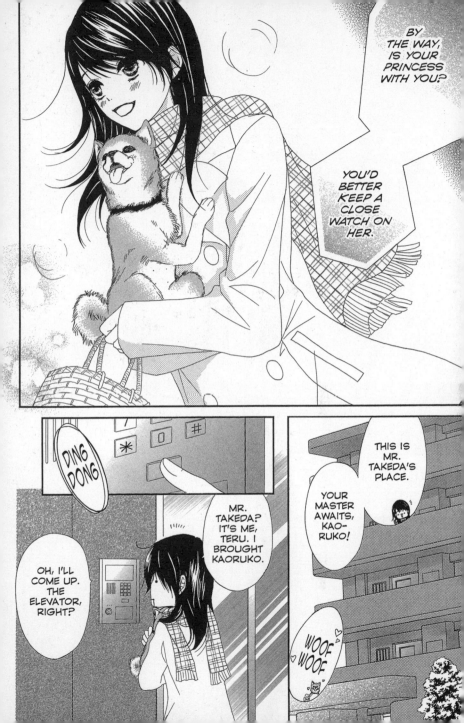

One must express oneself totally.

OH, TERU, SORRY FOR IGNORING YOU. BUT THIS IS OUR DAILY RITUAL.

PANT PANT

I guess the greeting ritual is very important.

DON'T MIND ME. I'VE HEARD HOW DOG LOVERS USUALLY ACT.

MY DOG IS THE BEST!!

HARUKA AND KAKO ALWAYS BRAG ABOUT THEIR FAMILY DOGS TOO.

I MISSED YOU SO MUCH! YOU ARE THE CUTEST THING IN THE WHOLE WORLD.

YOU WENT FOR A WALK, RIGHT? DID YOU POOP, LITTLE ANGEL?!

OHHHH, YOU CAME HOME, MY KAORUKO. MY LITTLE ANGEL KAORUKO!

OHHH

OHHH

OHHH

OH

THIS IS SUCH A NICE PLACE.

OH, THANKS.

THANK YOU FOR INVITING ME. WOW...

KAORUKO, I'LL FEED YOU IN A MINUTE.

I just ground some beans.

I'LL MAKE YOU MY SPECIAL COFFEE.

SIT ANYWHERE, TERU.

I SPOKE TO KUROSAKI. DID HE COME ON TO YOU?

HE SOUNDED GUILT-RIDDEN AND RAMBLED ON ABOUT NEVER DRINKING AGAIN.

Sorry about yesterday. I'm a little embarrassed.

I WOKE UP WITH A HANGOVER AND JUST TOOK A SHOWER.

I THOUGHT YOU LOOKED DIFFERENT TODAY... IT'S YOUR HAIR.

It makes you look less strict.

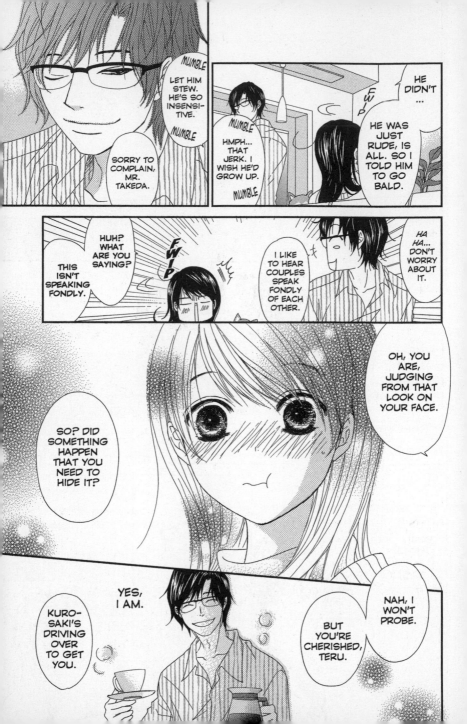

"I AM DRUNK. THAT'S WHY I CAN BE HONEST ABOUT MY FEELINGS."

"I DEPEND ON YOU."

ACTUALLY, I'M NOT UPSET WITH KUROSAKI...

...ABOUT LAST NIGHT.

I FELT NERVOUS AND SHY AND HAPPY.

BUT FALLING ASLEEP ON ME LIKE THAT WAS RUDE.

BLUSH

I'M VERY HAPPY.

YES...

I'M SO CHERISHED.

Kaoruko, here's your breakfast.

Enjoy, enjoy.

THIS HAPPINESS CAN'T BE TAKEN FOR GRANTED.

IT'S BEYOND THE NORM THE WAY EVERYONE QUIETLY WATCHES OVER THIS DELICATE RELATIONSHIP I HAVE WITH KUROSAKI.

Don't you dare take advantage of her during the night!

Mmm, it smells so good.

Thank you.

I MUSTN'T EVER FORGET.

*ONE EXAMPLE OF QUIETLY WATCHING

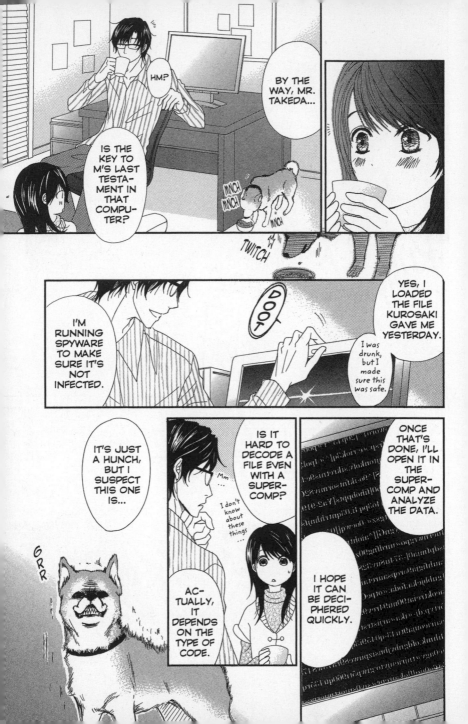

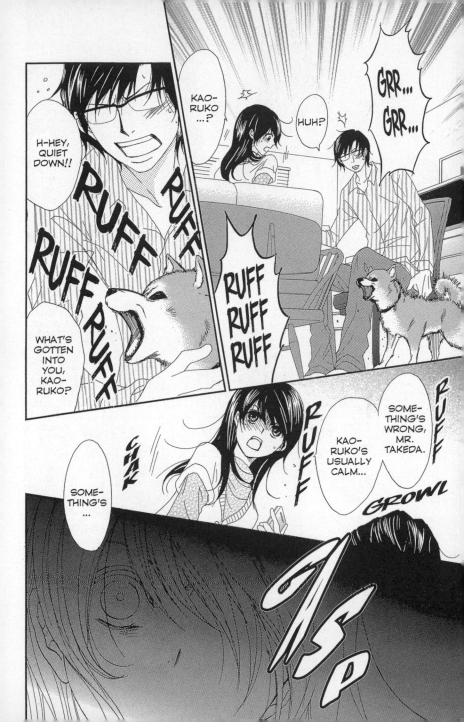

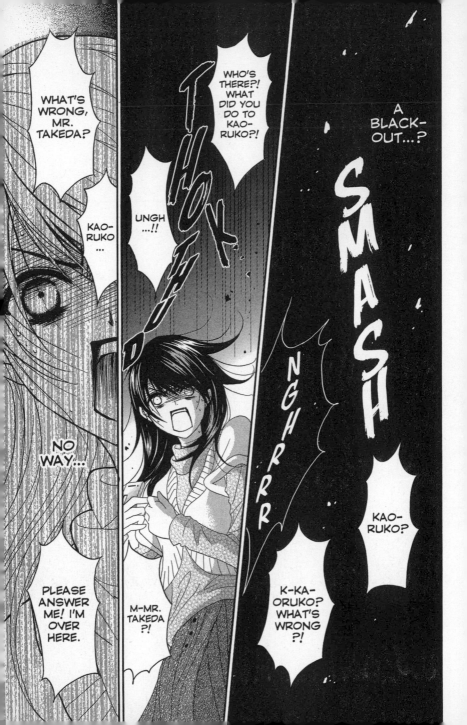

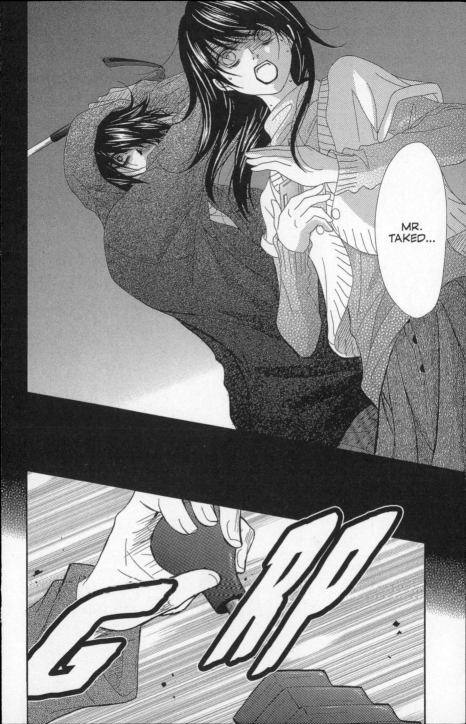

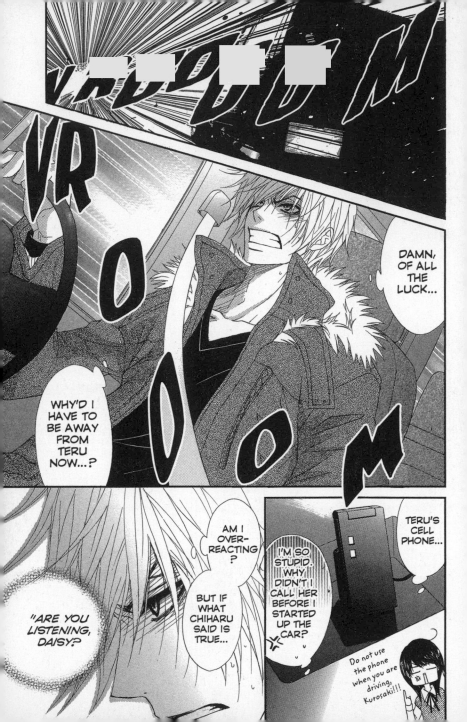

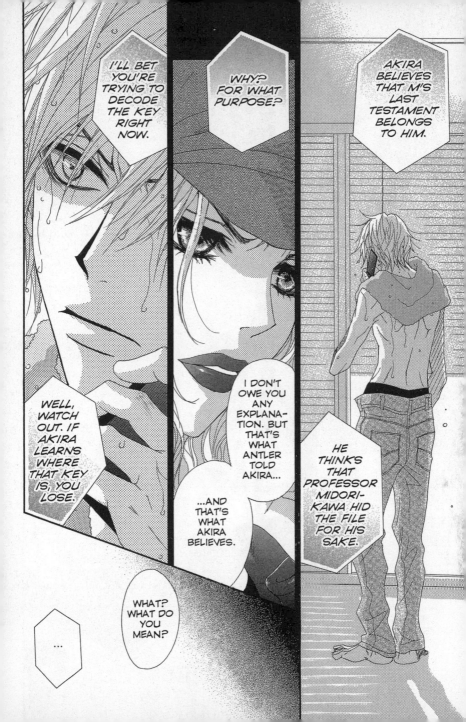

IT'S AKIRA'S SPECIALITY.

YOU KNOW WHAT I'M TALKING ABOUT, DON'T YOU, DAISY?

"THAT BOY WILL DO ANYTHING TO GET HIS HANDS ON M'S LAST TESTAMENT.

"HE DOESN'T CARE ABOUT...

"...WHO OR WHAT HE HARMS..."

BE
EEP

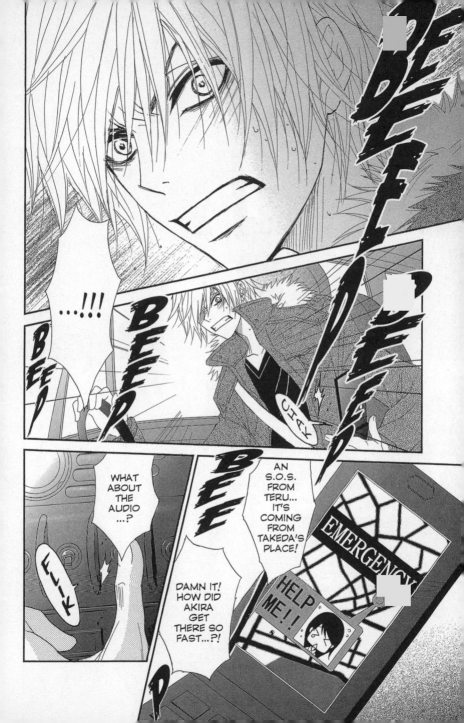

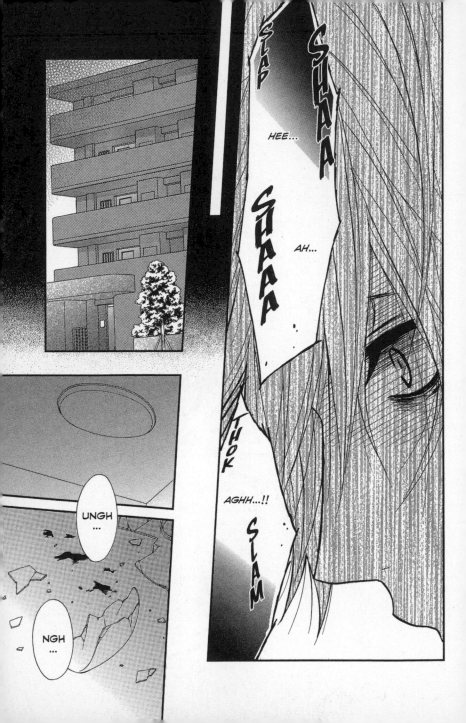

WHEEZE

WHEEZE

I'M BLEED-ING, DAMN YOU...

NHN... OWW... IT BURNS...

WHAT THE HELL...?

AGH, IT HURTS...

WHAT THE HELL DID YOU DO...?!

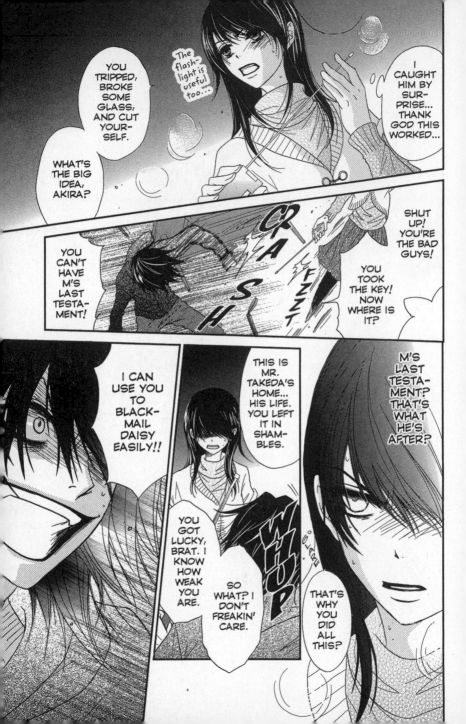

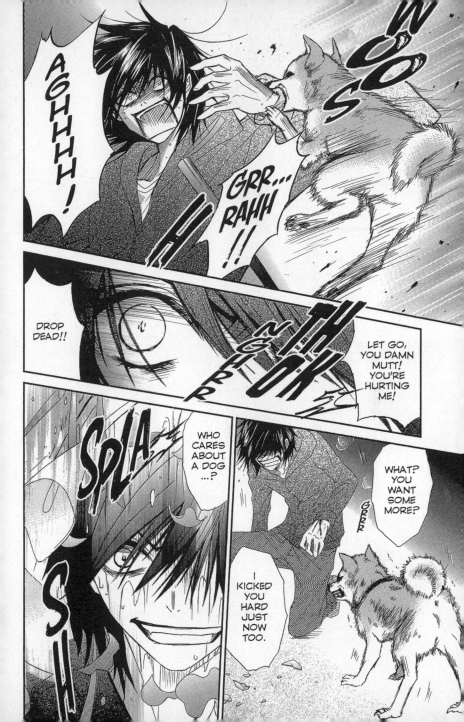

BUT I DON'T FEEL AFRAID.

YOU'RE WET. SO YOU KNOW WHAT'LL HAPPEN, RIGHT?

HE'S JUST AS DESPERATE AS LAST TIME.

WONDER WHY?

HUH?

HA HA... THAT'S SO STUPID. YOU'RE BLUFFING.

CUT IT OUT.

DON'T MOVE.

I SET THIS TO MAXIMUM POWER.

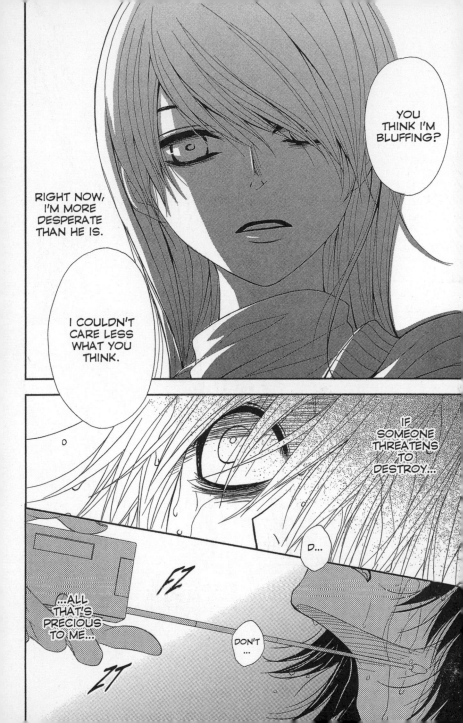

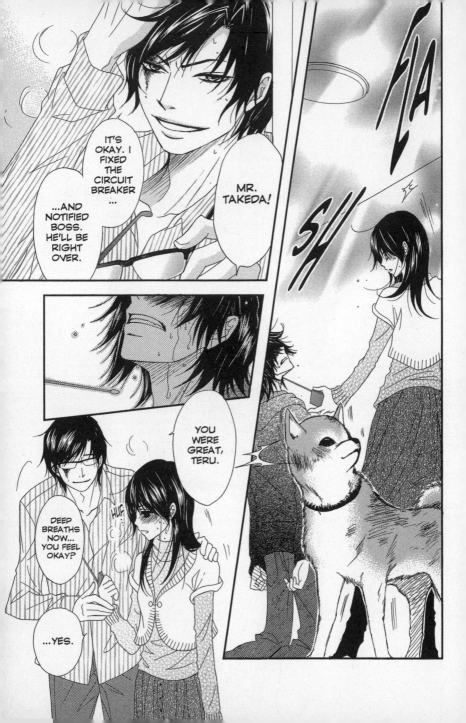

I'm so proud of you.

You're a good girl.

Are you okay, Kaoruko?

NGH... HIC...

UNGH... NGH...

THUD

DON'T WORRY, TERU. YOUR TRICK WORKED.

R-RIGHT.

LET'S LEAVE HIM. BOSS AND KUROSAKI CAN TAKE CARE OF THE REST.

TRMBL TRMBL

...DON'T WANNA DIE. UHN...

SNIFF

HELP ME... I'M SCARED ...

NGH... UGH...

HIC... NO...

I'D BETTER CHECK THE COMPUTER.

THE POWER WAS OUT SUDDENLY, SO I HOPE IT DIDN'T CORRUPT THE DATA.

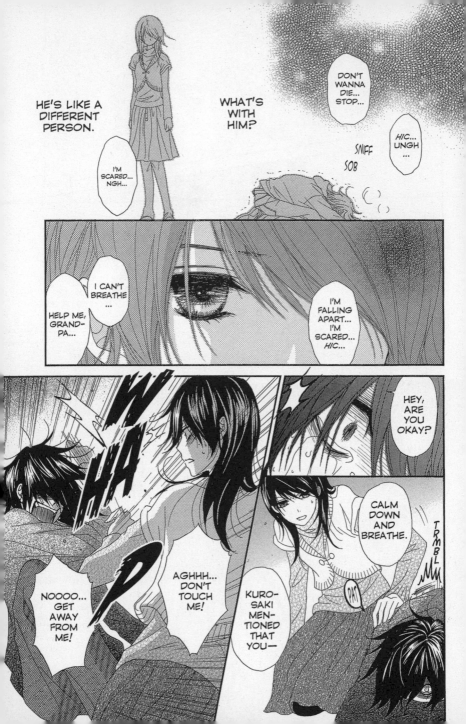

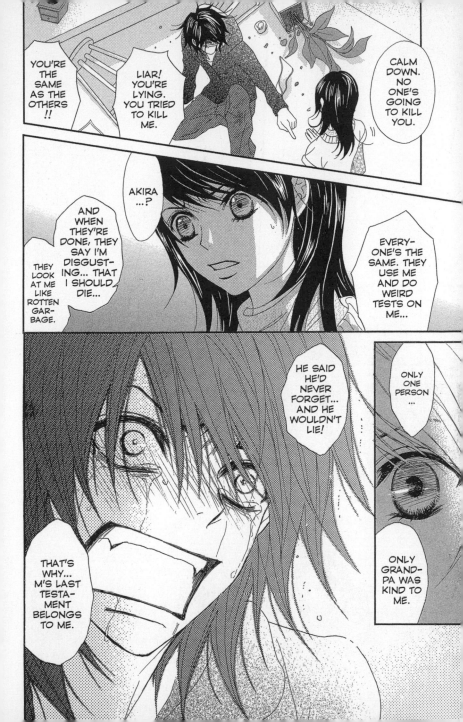

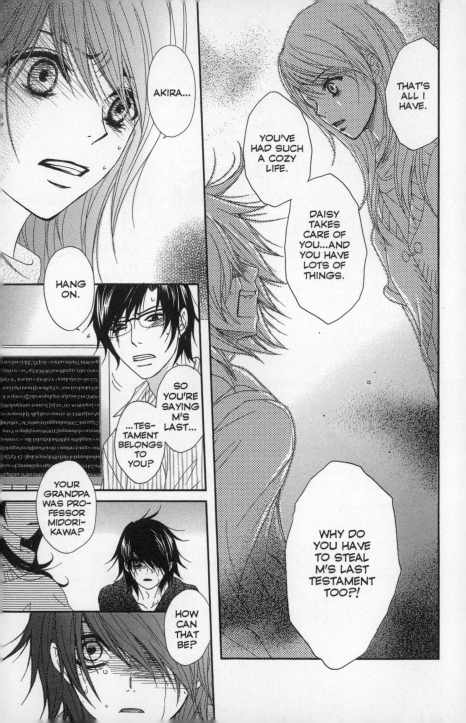

THE PROFESSOR HAD NO KIN.

CERTAINLY NOT A GRAND-SON...

0-93-13P9ur49anpqr&k&:;d[^.a-^ero3wopyreo
oo03e-wr^]9rp[wsworcyr20erruhjilgil;sh]kbwaro:
9e-frmua[3cwwri[90-1rxbhvqhjslfd]iaYw3io[a[wi
y&82C08r^q-Iscikrsopeurru[2^1^Y-ewa]o1p]
r3-9193u-f49uwqbhvsilofoxizho03rc9a0ucrijisdic
hbhjismkj;xznavis;z iero-w8q923r8r9h6wtj]iu
rw3-1020-urjwaopefjnodsuljufbyhbkldo:o: es[a]2d
r17j7yf4973g9jgisiolnopaichv nq0klsm :iVeC90shnqu9erso[tu
57&c7vrhhaop329-91^9+-qwa-peotk[;sdailjivglsubnav;a: sdl:lir
90u33-10urruwo-tc[n&9rgn[dib]]g9-rsc-[Q-picrrYsrbdjfgior
a aueveramiro0acire-a9o-raojcino0nub09lsurm rm0a9re^aC0&m
ijeS[hrgskrtoprhaYpsaAdhd9e0p-irsoeik[f-dk
jlllojupsamlas;x[-g[al][aY-pcirhjifjlogjlt&urr

EVEN IF WE WERE TO GIVE IT TO YOU...

BESIDES, THE KEY IS EN-CODED.

MR. TAKEDA, THE DATA ON THE KEY...?

AKIRA, I CAN'T GIVE YOU THE KEY.

WE NEED IT OUR-SELVES.

OH, EVERY-THING'S INTACT.

HEE HEE...

72

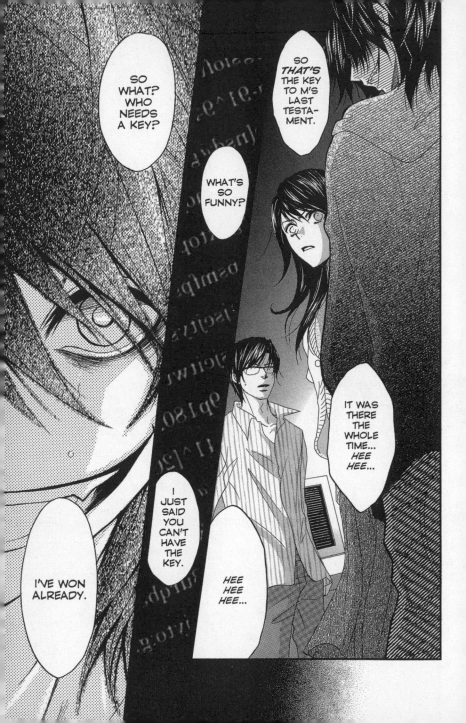

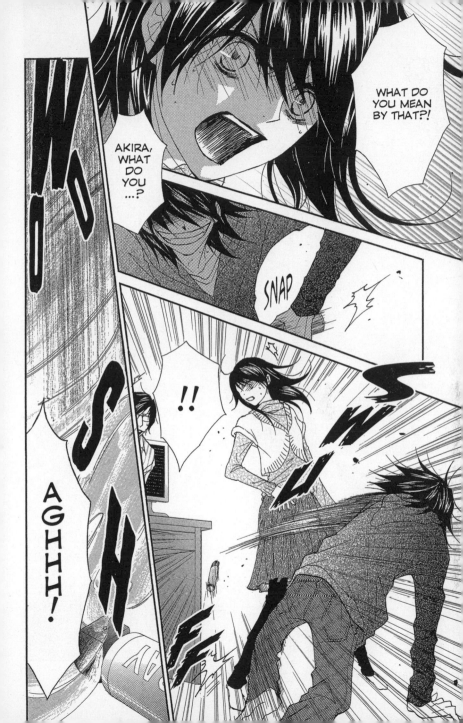

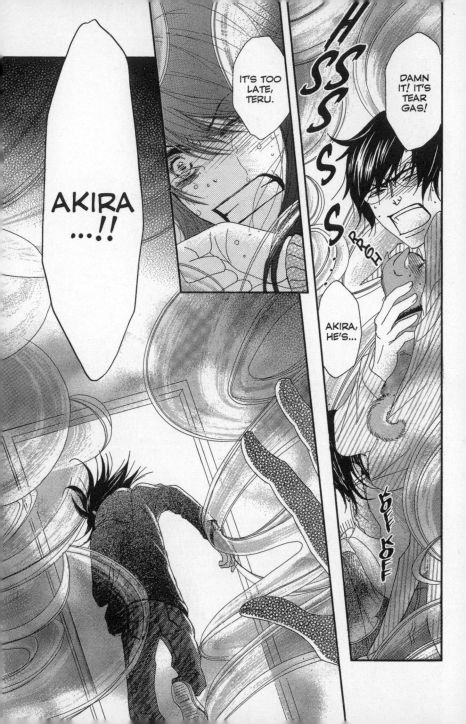

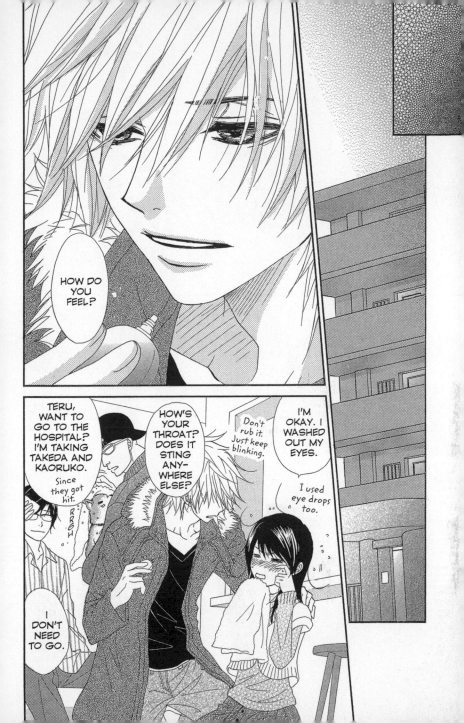

SORRY I WAS LATE.

BMP

YOU DID GOOD.

TAKEDA, SORRY YOU HAD TO GO THROUGH THIS.

We'll pay for the damages.

NO, I KNEW WHAT TO EXPECT WHEN I AGREED TO THIS.

I WISH I COULD'VE SPARED KAORUKO THOUGH.

You should've seen my princess in action.

BUT IT'S STRANGE...

I'M SORRY THAT AKIRA...

WE CAN'T HELP THAT HE GOT AWAY.

Don't worry about it.

THE KEY IS SAFE. THAT'S THE MAIN THING.

AKIRA LOOKED AT THE DATA, THEN SAID HE DIDN'T NEED IT.

HE MUST'VE LOOKED AT IT FOR A SECOND, BUT HE STARTED LAUGHING.

HE SAID THAT HE'D WON...

HUH?

BEFORE THAT, HE WAS CRYING AND SO UPSET...

HE MUST HAVE SOLVED IT.

AKIRA HAS THIS ABILITY...

AN UNBELIEVABLE, UNCANNY KNACK...

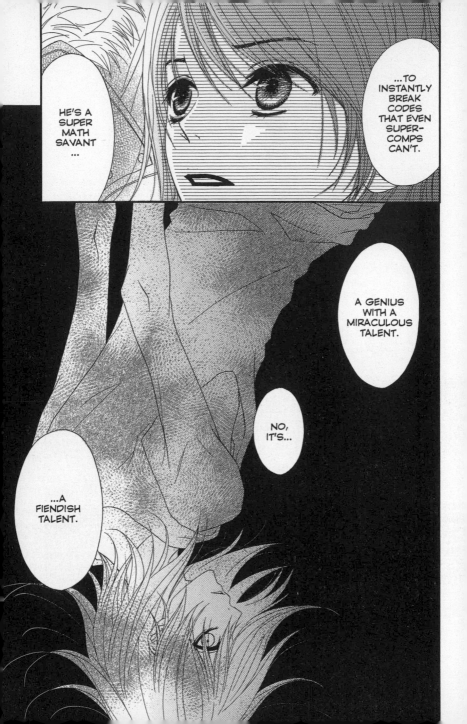

RELOCATED → BALDLY ASK!!! ②

DURING THE STUDY TRIP IN VOLUME 3, TERU GETS UPSET AT A MESSAGE SHE RECEIVES FROM KUROSAKI AND HURLS HER CELL PHONE. THE FOLLOWING DAY, SHE CALLS HIM. SO DID SHE GO AND PICK UP HER PHONE? ALSO WHEN WILL KUROSAKI GO BALD?

(DAISY, SHIMANE PREFECTURE)

I HADN'T GOTTEN ANY KUROSAKI-GOING-BALD QUESTIONS LATELY, SO THIS MADE ME VERY HAPPY. THANK YOU. AND THE CELL WAS PICKED UP. BY YOSHI.

DURING THAT TIME AT THE HOTEL WHEN THEY SHARED A ROOM (VOLUME 9, CHAPTER 42), DID KUROSAKI ENGAGE IN PERVERTED BEHAVIOR? FRANKLY, I WISH HE DID.

(Y.K., OSAKA)

HMM... WHY DON'T I LEAVE THAT TO YOUR IMAGINATION? HE DID RECITE THE SUTRA THOUGH. ANYWAY, TERU'S A DEEP SLEEPER, AND HE PROBABLY WENT AS FAR AS BLOWING INTO HER EAR... ER, NEVER MIND.
BY THE WAY, THIS IS THE INSERT THAT WAS IN *BETSUCOMI* MAGAZINE BACK THEN. ──────→
IT'S OBVIOUS THAT THE EDITORS DIDN'T TRUST KUROSAKI AT ALL.
THIS PAGE DOESN'T HAVE A HINT OF VULGARITY...YET IT RAISED CONSIDER-ABLE SUSPICION (IN THE SUGGESTIVE SENSE).
EDITOR S, WHO WROTE THIS, CURRENTLY WORKS AT ANOTHER MAGAZINE. (HOW ARE YOU? TAKE CARE OF YOUR BOOBS.)
CURRENTLY, EDITOR F AND HER FINE TEAM HAVE KEPT *DAISY* GOING FULL STEAM. THE MAGAZINE HAS LOTS OF OTHER GREAT PROJECTS, SO BESIDES THE GRAPHIC NOVEL, PLEASE TRY READING *BETSUCOMI*.

ENLARGED ↓

WITH HIS FREE LEFT HAND, DID KUROSAKI READ THE SUTRA OR DID HE...? IN THE NEXT ISSUE, "JF" IS ON THE MOVE!

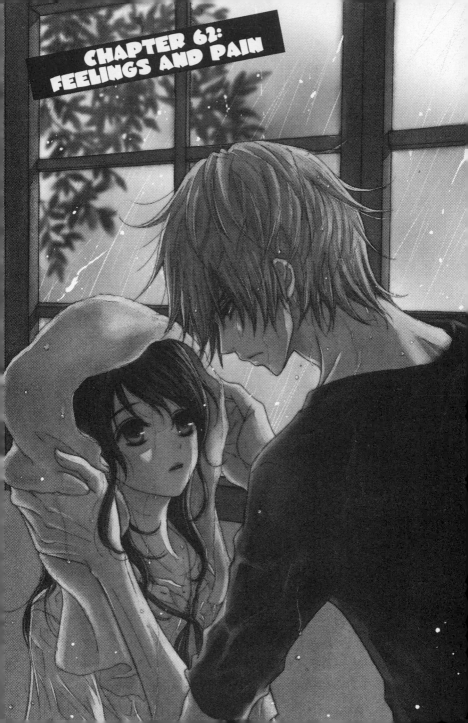

CHAPTER 62:
FEELINGS AND PAIN

"ONLY GRANDPA WAS KIND TO ME.
"HE SAID HE'D NEVER FORGET... AND HE WOULDN'T LIE!
"SO THAT'S THE KEY...
"IT WAS THERE THE WHOLE TIME...
"THAT'S WHY... M'S LAST TESTAMENT BELONGS TO ME."
"I'VE WON ALREADY!"

HE DOESN'T CARE WHO HE HURTS.

WHO DOES HE THINK HE IS?

AKIRA...

"WHY DO YOU HAVE TO STEAL M'S LAST TESTAMENT TOO?!"

"YOU'VE HAD SUCH A COZY LIFE.

"EVERY-ONE'S THE SAME. THEY LOOK AT ME LIKE ROTTEN GARBAGE... AND SAY I SHOULD DIE."

STOP PLAYING THE VICTIM.

WHY...?

DON'T ACT LIKE WE'RE TO BLAME FOR IT ALL.

REGARDING TERU'S CELL PHONE WEAPON, "THE SHOCK-TENNA"... SHE SAID SHE SET IT TO "MAXIMUM POWER," BUT THAT WAS **A BIG ACT.**

IT'S JUST A LITTLE SHOCK, LIKE THE KIND YOU GET WHEN YOU TOUCH A DOORKNOB IN WINTERTIME.

UNDER-STAND THIS!

CHANCES ARE VERY LOW, BUT ONCE IN A WHILE, IT MIGHT WORK, MAYBE LIKE IN A MINOR GAME OF MAHJONG.

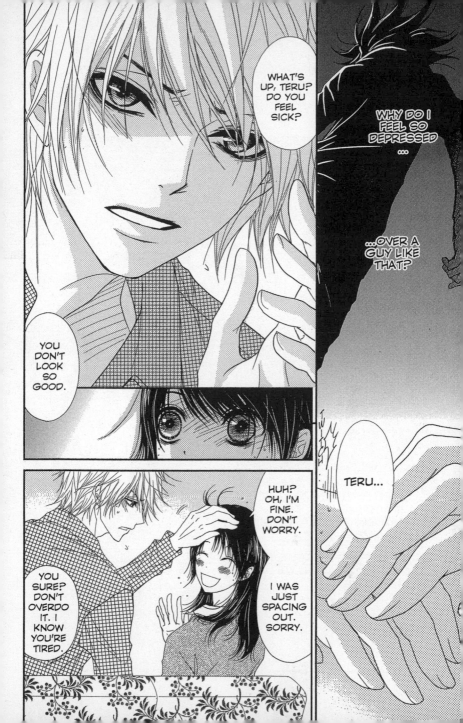

EVERYONE'S SERIOUS HERE. THIS ISN'T PLAYTIME, AND YOU NEED TO FOCUS.

PAY ATTENTION, WILL YOU?

HEY, YOU TWO.

HER BEING SO CHUMMY WITH A CRIMINAL MAKES ME WORRY ABOUT SECURITY.

SHE DOESN'T GET SPECIAL TREATMENT JUST BECAUSE SHE'S A KID.

THAT'S NO WAY TO TALK, SHIBAYAMA. TERU'S JUST—

S-SORRY...

AN EMERGENCY MEETING WAS HELD TO SHARE INFORMATION.

THE PARTICIPANTS WERE OUR USUAL GROUP...

THIS IS GOING NO-WHERE. MR. NISHIDA, PLEASE TAKE OVER.

GRAB

..!!

NOTHING WE DISCUSS GOES OUT OF THIS ROOM.

YES, I APOLOGIZE.

WATCH WHAT YOU SAY, SHIBAYAMA. THAT WAS UNNECESSARY.

MASUDA, CALM DOWN!

THE OTHERS SEEM TO KNOW THEM ALREADY.

HARD TO BELIEVE, BUT LET'S HEAR THEM OUT.

THE KEY TO IT MAY HAVE BEEN COMPROMISED.

I MET THEM FOR THE FIRST TIME.

...AND THESE PEOPLE FROM BOSS'S AGENCY...

THE SEARCH FOR M'S LAST TESTAMENT IS NOW URGENT.

I CAN'T PROVE IT, BUT...

...AKIRA IS A MATH SAVANT WHO CAN DECIPHER A CODE WITH ONE GLANCE.

KUROSAKI, CAN YOU TELL US...

...ABOUT THIS AKIRA FELLOW?

SURE.

86

NO MATTER HOW COMPLICATED OR HOW BIG THE PROBLEM IS, HE KNOWS THE ANSWER INSTANTLY.

A SUPER-COMPUTER IS NOTHING COMPARED TO HIM.

HE CAN DECRYPT A CODE WITH JUST ONE LOOK.

I DIDN'T UNDER-STAND...

...HOW FRIGHTENING AKIRA'S ABILITY WAS.

BUT THAT'S WHY ANTLER USED HIM.

CHATTER

IF SUCH A THING WERE POSSIBLE, SECURITY IN THE I.T. WORLD WOULD BE USELESS.

HOLD IT...

HE BROUGHT HYPERION DOWN TOO...

THE SOMBER MOOD TOLD ME JUST HOW DANGER-OUS HE WAS.

GIVE ME A BREAK. THAT STUFF BELONGS IN SCI-FI MOVIES.

WHY DIDN'T YOU TELL US SOONER, YOU IDIOT!

IF A MONSTER LIKE THAT STOLE THE DATA, IT'S OVER.

YOU KNEW ABOUT HIS ABILITY ALL THIS TIME, RIGHT?

"COULDN'T YOU FIGURE IT OUT?"

"DON'T BE SHOCKED. I JUST DECODED IT FOR YOU."

YOU PROBABLY DIDN'T BELIEVE IT EITHER.

DON'T BLAME KUROSAKI. WE SENT REPORT AFTER REPORT.

I WASN'T HIDING IT. I JUST COULDN'T BELIEVE IT.

THE FIRST TIME, I FIGURED HE HAD THE ANSWER BEFORE-HAND.

TH-THAT'S BECAUSE WE WERE WAITING FOR...

HEY, ARE YOU BLAMING ME NOW?!

BESIDES, AKIRA WAS ALREADY MARKED AS SOMEONE TO WATCH.

YET WE DIDN'T GET ANY REPORTS FROM ANYONE HIGHER UP.

TALK ABOUT CARE-LESS...

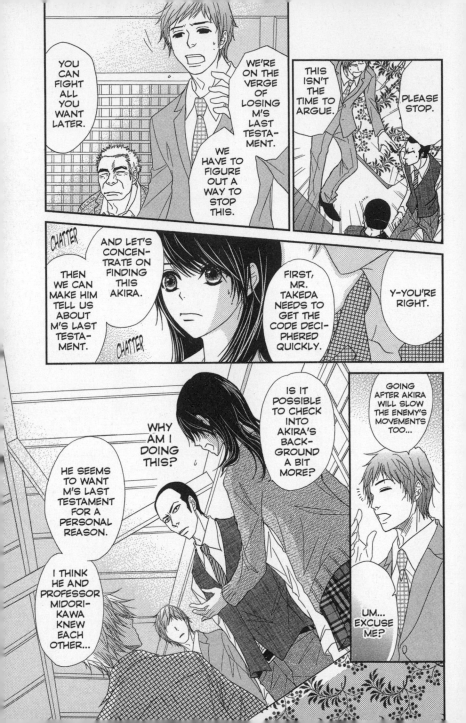

Kurosaki...

IS IT REALLY CHILDISH?

WON'T IT HELP US TO KNOW MORE ABOUT M'S LAST TESTAMENT?

WHERE'S YOUR COMMON SENSE? CHILDISH OPINIONS HAVE NO PLACE HERE.

SHOCK

OH, COME ON. THAT'S JUST A WASTE OF TIME.

OF COURSE...

CATCHING AKIRA DOESN'T GUARANTEE HE'LL TALK.

WE SHOULD LOOK FOR OPTIONS.

HEY, WHAT THE HELL?! YOU TAKE THAT BACK!

SHUT UP! IF HE'S NOT, THEN HE CAN SHOW ME PROOF!

I'VE NEVER LIKED THIS GUY ANYWAY!

WHY'RE YOU SO CONCERNED ABOUT AKIRA?

ARE YOU TWO WORKING TOGETHER?

WHAT'S WITH YOU?

90

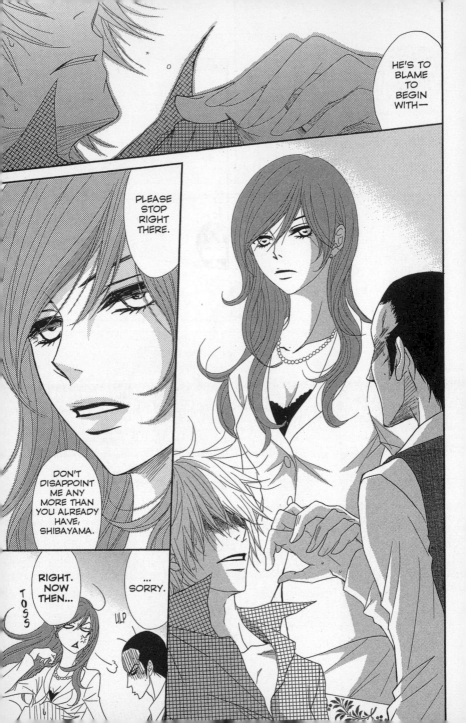

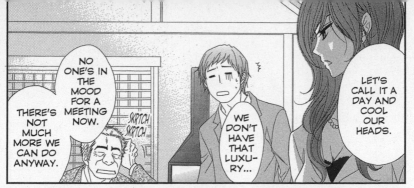

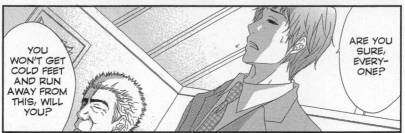

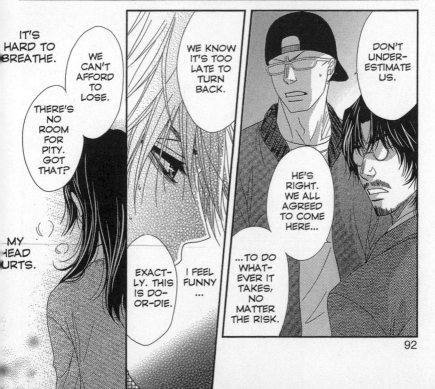

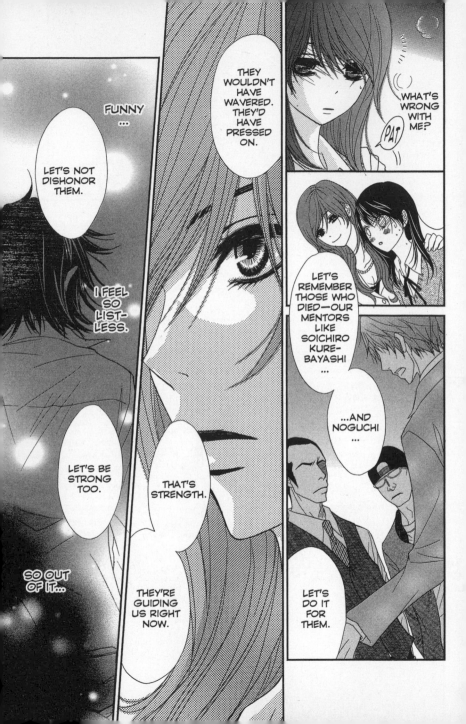

YOU HAVE A BIT OF A HIGH TEMPER-ATURE, TERU.

IT COUNTS AS A FEVER.

DIDN'T FEEL WELL OUT THERE, HUH?

FWUP

GET SOME REST.

SO MANY THINGS HAVE HAP-PENED. YOU'RE EX-HAUSTED.

NO WONDER I FELT WOOZY.

UGH. I HARDLY EVER GET SICK.

I was afraid it was a bad omen.

YOU LOOKED PALE DURING THE MEETING. POOR THING...

TURN

WHAT'S WITH ME?

I CAN'T STOP THINK- ING...

WHY ...?

I'M JUST MUMBLING TO MYSELF.

OH, IT'S NOTHING.

WHAT IS IT, TERU?

WHY APOLOGIZE ?

I-I'M SORRY. I SHOULD'VE KNOWN BETTER...

That started it all...

I RUINED THE MEETING.

I SHOULDN'T HAVE SAID ANYTHING. I'M SORRY.

YOU CAN'T STOP THINKING ABOUT AKIRA?

YOU BROUGHT HIM UP DURING THE MEETING.

OH, LIKE THAT MR. NOGUCHI?

I THINK I MENTIONED IT BEFORE.

They're all so immature.

YOU SEE, PEOPLE IN THE AGENCY HAVE LOST FRIENDS TOO.

EVERYONE'S ON EDGE.

IT'S OKAY.

YOU DID NOTHING WRONG.

AND HE GOT BAD POLITICIANS ARRESTED.

HE WENT THROUGH HOOPS TO GET KUROSAKI OUT.

...IN EXCHANGE FOR KUROSAKI'S FREEDOM.

IT WAS NOGUCHI WHO ASKED SOICHIRO TO DECIPHER THE CODE...

THE DATA HE GUARDED SO CAREFULLY WENT MISSING.

BUT HE SUDDENLY DISAPPEARED...AND WAS FOUND DEAD UNDER SUSPICIOUS CIRCUMSTANCES.

HE WAS HONEST AND TRUSTED BY THOSE WHO WORKED UNDER HIM.

THAT'S WHY SHIBAYAMA AND THE OTHERS ARE DETERMINED LIKE US...

MAYBE EVEN MORE SO.

THAT DATA IS M'S LAST TESTAMENT.

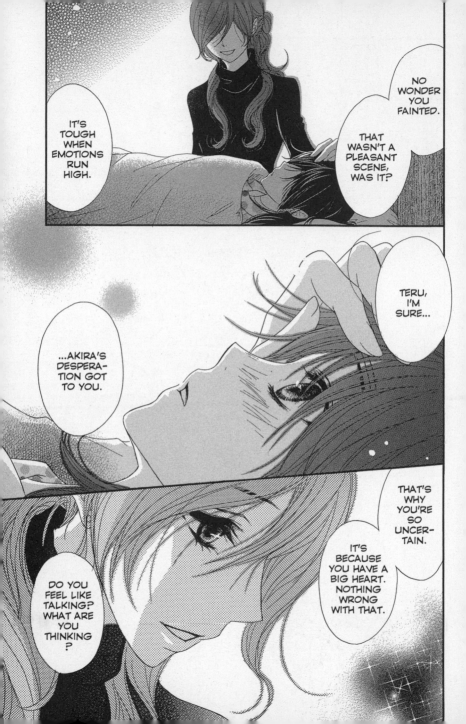

BUT HE'S WRONG. ACTING LIKE A VICTIM ALL OF A SUDDEN...

MM...

AKIRA HATES ME AND LOOKS DOWN ON ME. I DON'T LIKE HIM EITHER.

YES, YOU'RE RIGHT.

I DON'T KNOW WHY AKIRA SAID THOSE THINGS TO ME.

IT MAKES ME MAD.

WHO'D WANT TO HELP HIM?

HE'S DISGUSTING.

HE SAID NO ONE'S KIND TO HIM. IT'S EASY TO UNDERSTAND WHY.

I DON'T KNOW WHY...

...I'M CRYING.

OR WHY I'M SO UPSET...

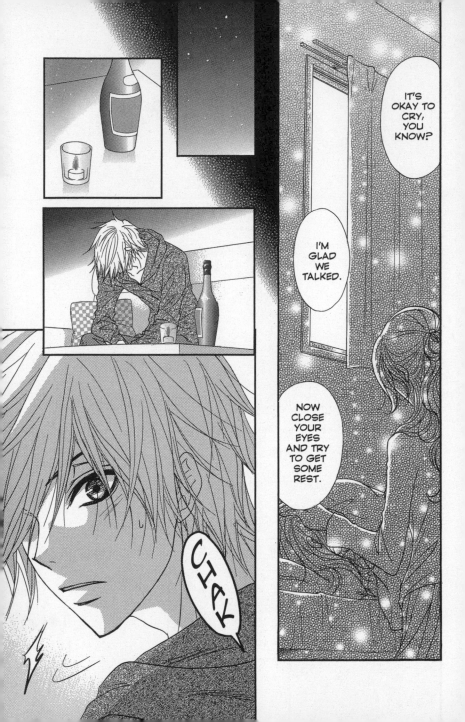

SHE GOT THINGS OFF HER CHEST. ALL SHE NEEDS NOW IS SLEEP.

ZZZ

SHE HAS A SLIGHT FEVER.

HOW'S TERU?

SHT

OKAY...

SLEEP-ING.

FAST ASLEEP AFTER A CRYING BOUT (IN SYSTEM RESTORE MODE)

NAH. YOU'VE BEEN WITH HER, SO I'M NOT WORRIED.

HO HO HO

WHAT? ARE YOU UPSET?

DON'T TELL ME YOU WANTED TO NURSE HER?

I GUESS I'LL GO.

GO LOOK IN ON HER.

I'll allow that much.

YOU WERE WORRIED ABOUT HER AT THE MEETING TOO.

WAIT.

SNAG

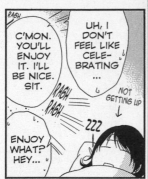
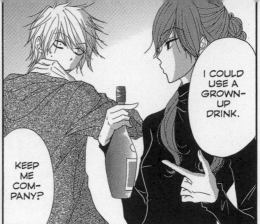
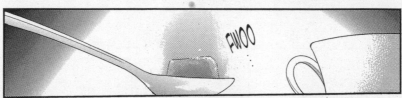
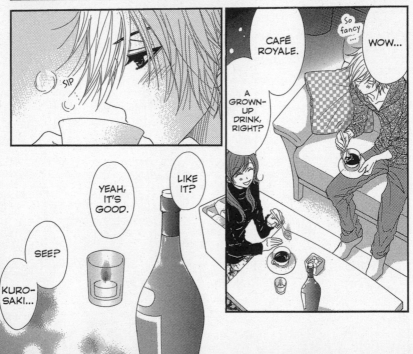

DON'T CALL ME BALD.

HEY, WOMAN.

HE'S MAKING IT A PERSONAL VENDETTA.

WELL, I DON'T BLAME HIM FOR HATING ME...

YOU MEAN SHIBA-YAMA?

THEY SAY HE'S SHORT-TEMPERED BUT BASI-CALLY GOOD...

Still, I can't forgive him.

WHAT THAT IDIOT SAID WAS RIDICU-LOUS.

DON'T LET THAT MEETING BOTHER YOU.

ANYWAY, YOU DID NOTHING WRONG.

IT WAS, PERHAPS...

ABOUT AKIRA?

ACTUALLY, I WAS WORRIED...

HA HA, SO THAT'S WHY YOU STOPPED ME... TO CONSOLE ME?

..UNNECESSARY.

THANKS, SIS.

TERU WAS WORRIED TOO.

...THAT MAYBE I SAID TOO MUCH.

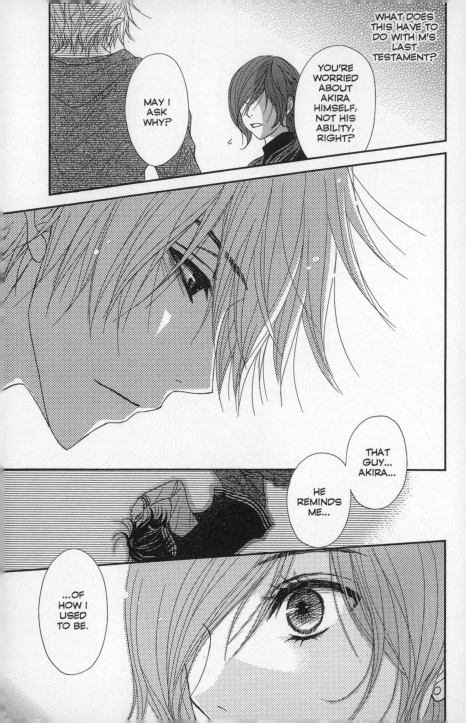

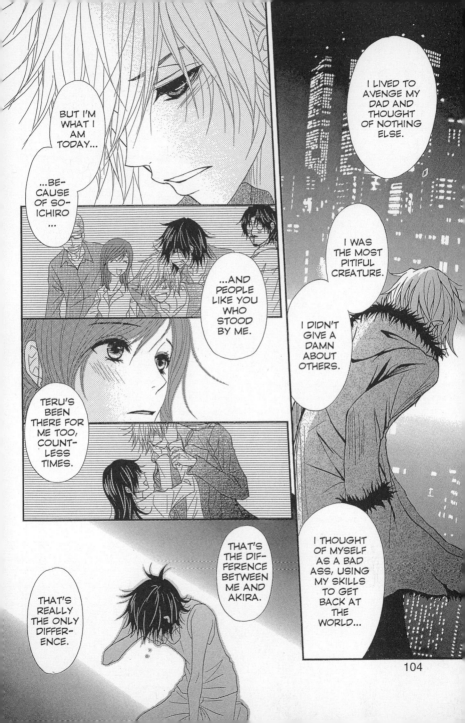

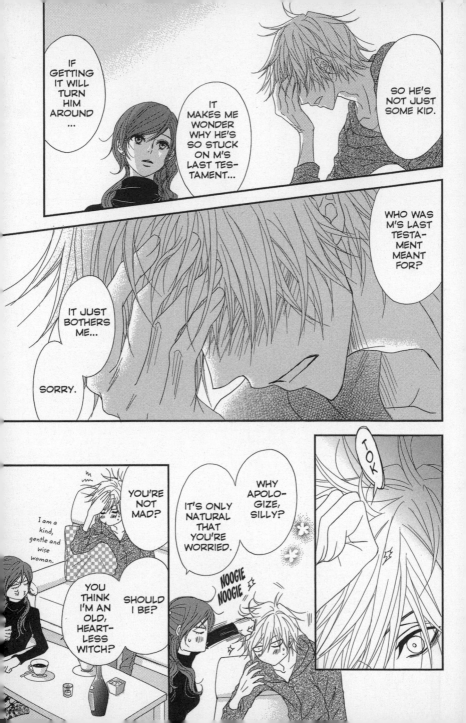

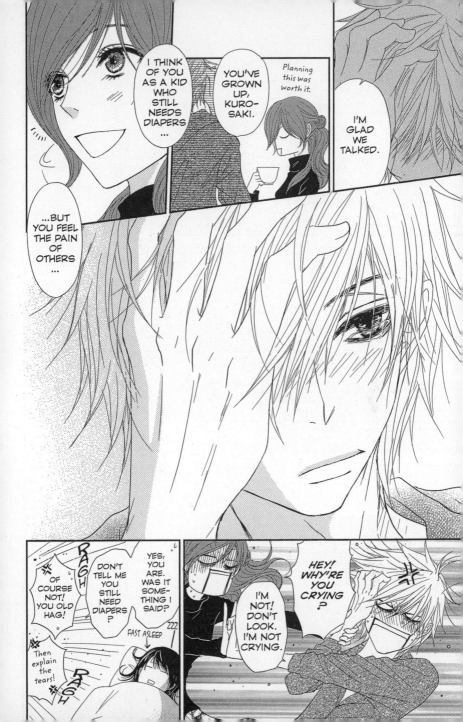

TO BE HONEST, I WAS SCARED.

I THOUGHT YOU'D BE DISAPPOINTED.

BOSS, ANDY...

I MEAN, EVERYONE'S DETERMINED TO GO FORWARD WITH M'S LAST TESTAMENT.

Scared? How old are you?

W-WHY?

WHAT? AS IF SOMETHING LIKE THAT...

...AND IF THAT BREAKS UP THE TEAM...

BUT TERU AND I HAVE BEEN THINKING DIFFERENTLY...

ARE WE TO BLAME?

DON'T BE SILLY.

DID WE GROWNUPS...

...MAKE IT IMPOSSIBLE FOR THEM TO SPEAK UP?

AND THAT'S BECAUSE WE DIDN'T WANT TO BE SEEN AS COWARDS OR TRAITORS...

...BY **SOMEONE.**

WE DECIDED WE COULDN'T TURN BACK.

WE DECIDED TO FIND M'S LAST TESTAMENT.

NO, IT'S TRUE.

DON'T TELL ANYONE I CRIED... ESPE-CIALLY TERU.

IT CAN'T BE...

SHE'S CONKED OUT, SO I KNOW SHE DIDN'T SEE...

DAMMIT... HOW CAN I BE SO WEAK?

I'm such an idiot.

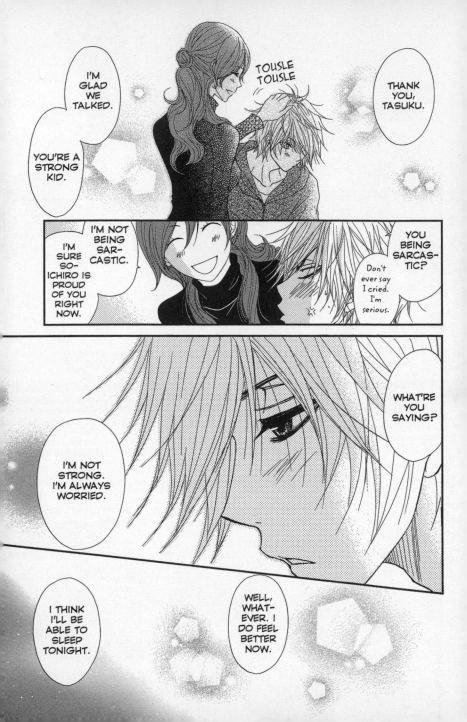

THANKS, RIKO.

I RELY ON YOU A LOT.

M'S LAST TESTA- MENT...

PROFESSOR MIDORI- KAWA LEFT US "SOME- THING."

SOICHIRO, WHO DIED, WAS INVOLVED WITH THAT "SOME- THING."

OTHER THAN THAT, WE KNOW ABSO- LUTELY NOTHING ...

THAT'S MY LINE.

紅林家之墓

*KUREBAYASHI FAMILY GRAVE

...WOULD PUT THESE SOULS TO REST.

GETTING AHOLD OF THAT "THING"...

THAT'S WHAT WE BELIEVED.

SO-ICHIRO...

OR DID SOMEONE PREVENT YOU FROM DOING THAT?

WERE YOU GOING TO SAY SOMETHING?

YOU DIED WITHOUT TELLING US ANYTHING ABOUT M'S LAST TESTAMENT.

I'M SORRY I FORGOT WHAT YOU USED TO SAY.

I'M SORRY, SOICHIRO... ARE YOU ANGRY?

WE DECIDED TO DO THIS FOR YOUR SAKE WITHOUT EVEN KNOWING WHAT YOU WANTED.

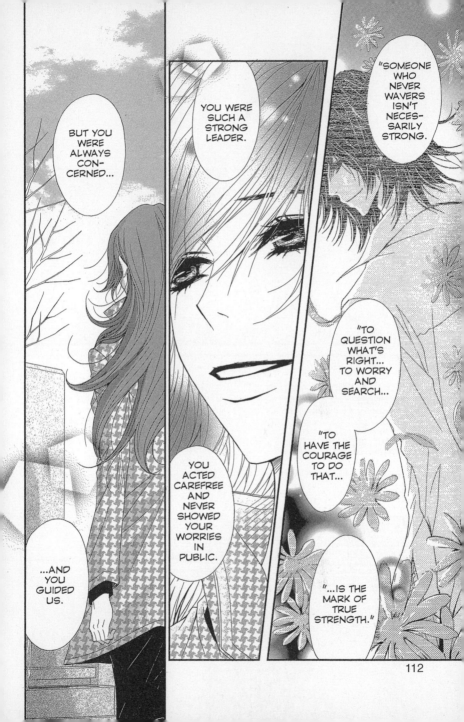

THAT WON'T DO, WILL IT?

UI-RA

THOSE KIDS DIDN'T NEED TO BE TOLD. THEY KNEW.

AM I STILL TRYING TO CLING TO YOU?

WE HAVE TO TAKE OVER FOR YOU...

...AND GUIDE THE YOUNGER GENERATION.

ISN'T THAT WHY WE GROW OLD?

RIKO.

KRZCH

NOT TO WORRY. WHAT'S THIS URGENT DISCUSSION ABOUT?

WHAT ABOUT KUROSAKI AND TERU?

SORRY TO CALL YOU OUT SO EARLY.

WHAT DO YOU MEAN?

I'LL EXPLAIN IN DETAIL LATER.

LET'S LISTEN TO IT AGAIN.

I HAVE A FEELING WE WERE SET UP.

BOSS...

YOU RECORDED ANTLER'S CALL, DIDN'T YOU?

YEAH, I SAVED IT.

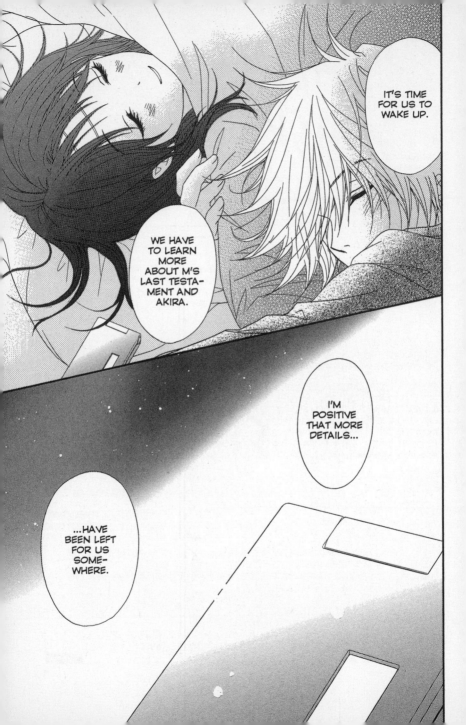

IS AKIRA RIGHT OR LEFT-HANDED? IN CHAPTER 44 WHILE PLAYING A GAME, HE HAS THE SIMULATION GUN IN HIS RIGHT HAND. SO I THOUGHT HE WAS RIGHT-HANDED. BUT IN CHAPTER 49, HE HITS TERU WITH HIS LEFT HAND AND HOLDS HIS POCKET KNIFE IN HIS LEFT HAND AS WELL. SO WHICH IS IT?

(RUI, OSAKA)

AKIRA IS AMBIDEXTROUS. I GUESS IT'S CONVENIENT WHEN PEOPLE CAN USE BOTH HANDS? ARE ANY OF YOU READERS AMBIDEXTROUS? BY THE WAY, I'M RIGHT-HANDED AND HEARD THAT HOLDING MY CHOPSTICKS IN MY LEFT HAND HELPS IN A DIET, SO I TRY IT SOMETIMES WHEN I REMEMBER. HMM... I DOUBT IF ANYONE CARES.

WHAT IS THE FAVORITE DS GAME OF THE CHARACTERS IN *DENGEKI DAISY*? (I'M ESPECIALLY CURIOUS ABOUT ANDY.)

(S.M., AICHI PREFECTURE)

I DON'T HAVE A DS... I'D LIKE TO TRY MONSTER HUNTER OR POKÉMON. (ACTUALLY, I'VE PROMISED TO PLAY WITH MY NIECE). BUT IF I GET HOOKED, *DENGEKI DAISY* MIGHT END RATHER QUICKLY. (AS IN, THE MANGA MIGHT BE DISCONTINUED). ANDY LIKES GAMES LIKE GYAKUTEN SAIBAN. I CAN SEE HIM AS THE GIRL WITH THE WHIP.

KUROSAKI HAS DEEP SIX-PACKS. WHEN AND WHY DOES HE TRAIN? DOES TERU LIKE GUYS WITH RIPPED ABS?

(Y.K., OSAKA)

HIS WORK REQUIRES PHYSICAL STRENGTH. ALSO, HE HAS TO PROTECT TERU AT ALL TIMES. AND IF TERU INADVERTENTLY SEES HIM, HE WANTS HER TO THINK, "HEY, KUROSAKI, YOU HAVE A NICE BOD... ARE YOU GOING TO HUG ME? I'M EXCITED...♡" SO HE TRAINS DILIGENTLY.

THINGS LIKE THAT MOTIVATE MEN.

ALSO, BOSS IS HIS TRAINER FOR FIGHTING TECHNIQUES AND BODY-BUILDING. TERU PREFERS RIPPED ABS. SHE ALSO BREAKS HER RICE CRACKER INTO PIECES BEFORE EATING THEM. THAT'S WHY I LIKE HER.

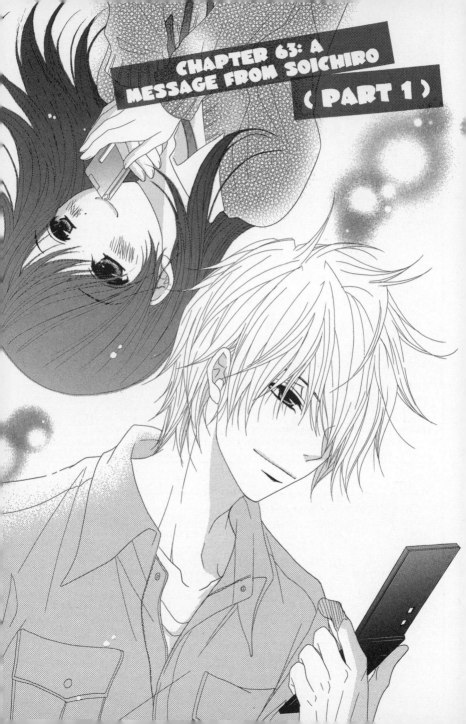

CHAPTER 63: A
MESSAGE FROM SOICHIRO
(PART 1)

OWW... MY BACK...

NHN... SO BRIGHT...

IT'S MORNING...?

WHEN DID I FALL ASLEEP...?

THE MOVIE TITLE IS "EIGHT GATES OF THE SHINOBI" AND IT'S GOTTEN GREAT REVIEWS DUE TO ITS USE OF PRACTICAL EFFECTS AND LIVE ACTION (RATHER THAN COMPUTER-GENERATED EFFECTS). THE HERO'S SIDEKICK, A NINJA CAT, IS OUTRAGEOUSLY CUTE AND HAS DIE-HARD FANS.

EIGHT GATES OF THE SHINOBI

I WONDER IF YOU READERS NOTICED THIS HANGING CASUALLY IN TERU'S ROOM? IT'S A COOL MOVIE POSTER THAT TERU PUT UP. HER WISH IS TO BECOME A NINJA SOMEDAY. THERE WASN'T MUCH ROOM FOR LAUGHTER IN THIS VOLUME, BUT MY ULTRA-TALENTED ASSISTANT WRACKED HER BRAINS TO COME UP WITH THIS. THANK YOU, M-SUKO!

GR

WAIT! LISTEN TO ME...

AHH...

AB

OH

FINALLY REMEMBERS THE NIGHT BEFORE

O-OH YEAH... DON'T WORRY. NOTHING BAD HAPPENED.

YOU HAD A FEVER AND RIKO WAS HERE AND—

I'M GOING TO GET UP NOW.

I NEED TO FRESHEN UP AND CHANGE...

SHOCK

?!?!?! WHAT THE—?! WHAT HAPPENED HERE?!

GOOD MORN-ING.

SHIELD

THAT IS WHAT I WOULD LIKE TO KNOW.

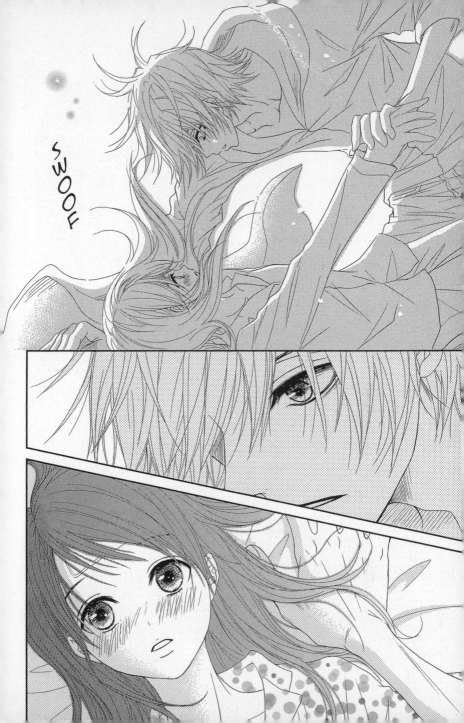

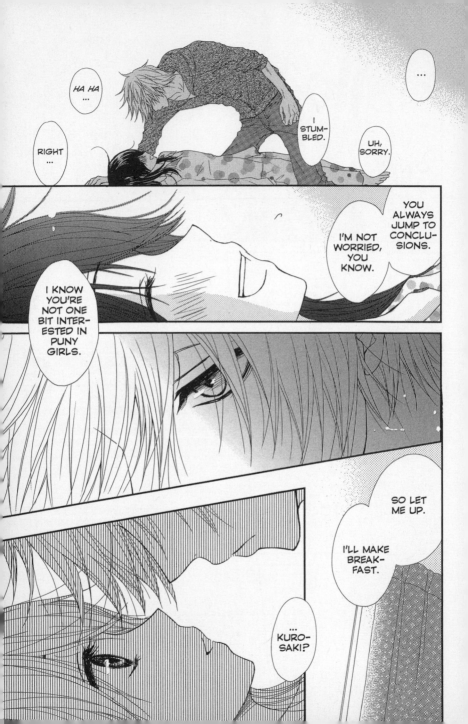

RIIP

OWW!

NEVER FORGET THAT MASTER KUROSAKI IS THE ULTIMATE BRUTE.

YOUR FEVER'S GONE. SO GET UP AND GET DRESSED.

FINE! CAN YOU MAKE SOME TOAST, AT LEAST?

POUT

WHAT'S THE BIG IDEA?! GO BALD, KUROSAKI!

I hope your hair falls out!

HOT TEA! WITH LOTS OF CREAM.

WILL INSTANT COFFEE DO?

FINE, GOT IT.

Yeah, yeah.

HMPH.

SLAM

IDIOT.

I WAS TEACHING YOU TO ALWAYS BE PRE-PARED.

YOU HAD MY HEART RACING FOR A MOMENT THERE.

HMPH...

TERU, HOW ARE YOU FEELING? I NEED TO GO OUT FOR A BIT. I'LL TALK TO YOU LATER. KUROSAKI

YEAH ...

DID YOU TALK ABOUT AKIRA?

SORRY I FELL ASLEEP.

RIKO'S NOT HERE?

LOOKS LIKE SHE LEFT.

HOW'D YOU GUESS?

I GUESS I FELT RELIEVED AFTER TALKING TO RIKO.

I WAS GONNA LOOK IN ON YOU, THEN LEAVE...

...WHY HE'S SO PASSION-ATE ABOUT M'S LAST TESTAMENT...

I WONDER WHAT HE'S PLANNING...

WELL...

HE'S BEEN ON MY MIND TOO.

HE WOULDN'T WANT MY PITY...

I'VE BEEN SO LUCKY. I CAN'T EVEN IMAGINE WHAT HE'S BEEN THROUGH.

...ABOUT HIS SPECIAL ABILITY, AND WHAT KIND OF LIFE HE'S HAD.

...YOU THINK ABOUT HIM A LOT.

SO...

...BUT I CAN'T HELP BUT FEEL THAT IT MEANS SOMETHING...

HM...

HM...

N-NO...

IT'S NONE OF MY BUSINESS.

HEY, THAT'S FINE BY ME.

FUU

HUH? KURO-SAKI...

SHOCK

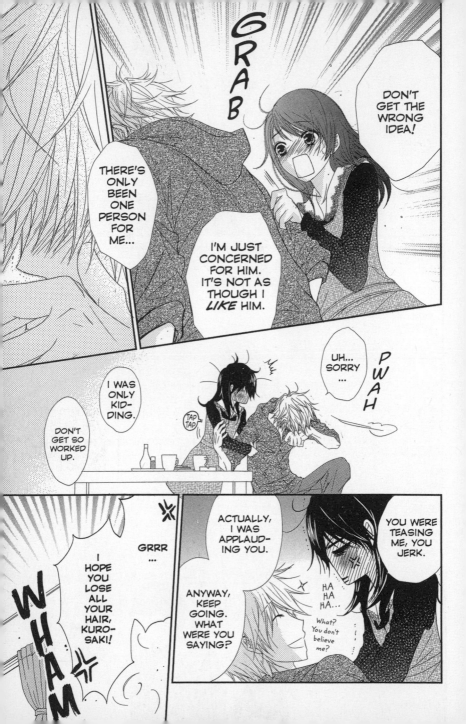

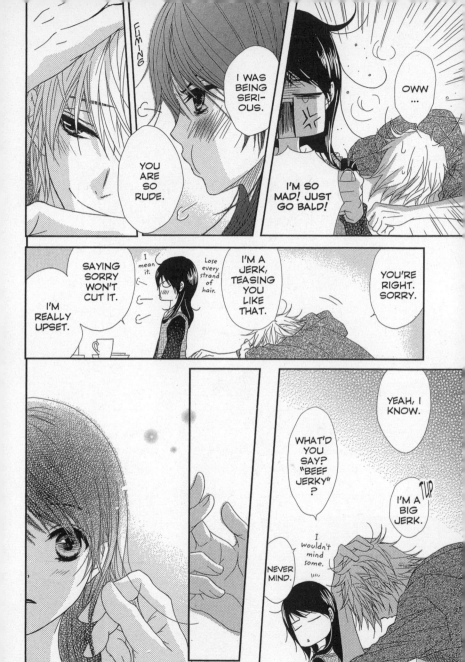

WHY'RE YOU TOUCH-ING ME?

W-WHAT IS IT?

I JUST WANT TO.

NO REASON.

CAN I?

THINK SO?

HEY, YOUR HAIR'S GOTTEN LONG.

YOU'RE RIGHT. SORRY.

YOU CAN. BUT YOU SHOULDN'T.

NOT.

THAT'S RIGHT. AND YOU WERE ALREADY BALDING.

IT WAS MUCH SHORTER WHEN WE FIRST MET.

YEAH.

YOU STILL TREAT ME LIKE YOUR SERVANT.

TERU...

AND YOU WERE ONLY KIND TO ME IN YOUR MES-SAGES.

HA HA...

I DIDN'T REALIZE YOU WERE DAISY AT ALL.

ULP

YEAH?

OH...

RRRING

HELLO? HEY, RIKO.

I WAS EXPECTING YOUR CALL. WE'RE READY.

RRRING

YEAH, SHE'S FINE. HER FEVER'S GONE... OKAY.

RRRING

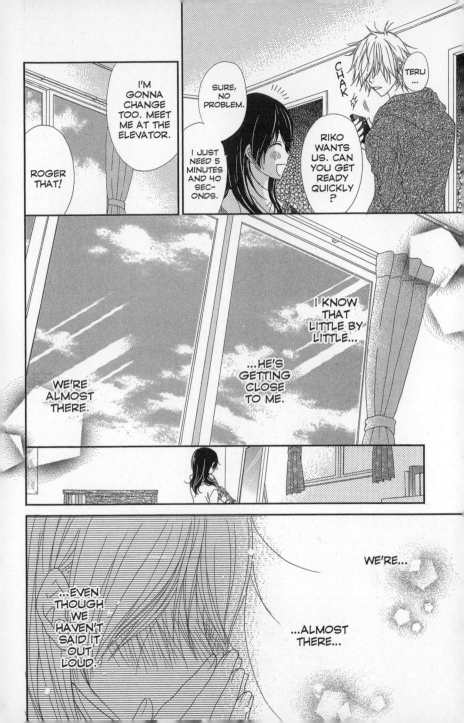

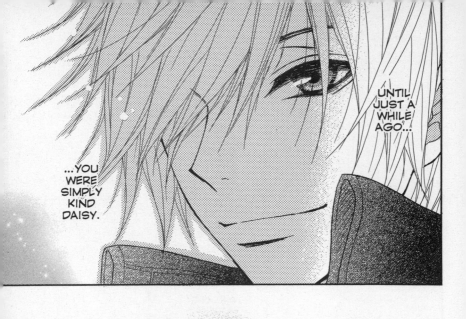

UNTIL
JUST A
WHILE
AGO...

...YOU
WERE
SIMPLY
KIND
DAISY.

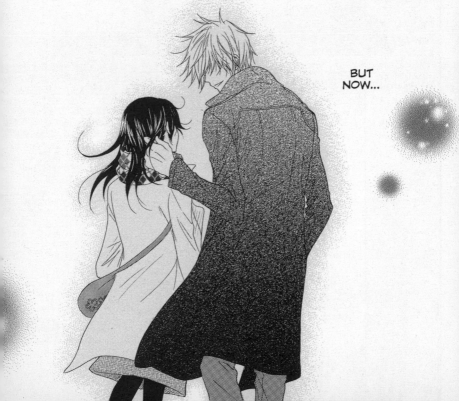

BUT
NOW...

OH, TASUKU AND TERU. YOU'RE EARLY.

CONGRATS ON THE RENOVATION, BOSS!

I helped with the design.

No one can break in. The windows are bulletproof. Oh, and the floors are heated.

Ho ho ho...

IT DOESN'T LOOK ANY DIFFERENT.

JUST WHO DO YOU EXPECT TO FIGHT?

NEVER MIND THAT. THE FOCUS WAS ON CONVENIENCE AND SECURITY.

SURE, BUT...

WHY THE SUDDEN CHANGE?

INSTEAD OF FOCUSING ON FINDING M'S LAST TESTAMENT, LET'S GATHER MORE INFO AND ANALYZE THE DATA.

ANYWAY, LET'S START OUR MEETING.

WELL...

THIS INCLUDES INFO ON AKIRA.

I WANT TO CHANGE OUR TEAM'S PLAN REGARDING M'S LAST TESTAMENT.

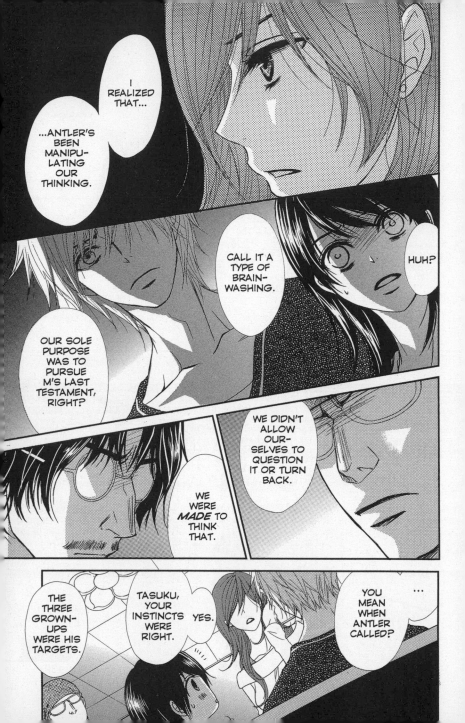

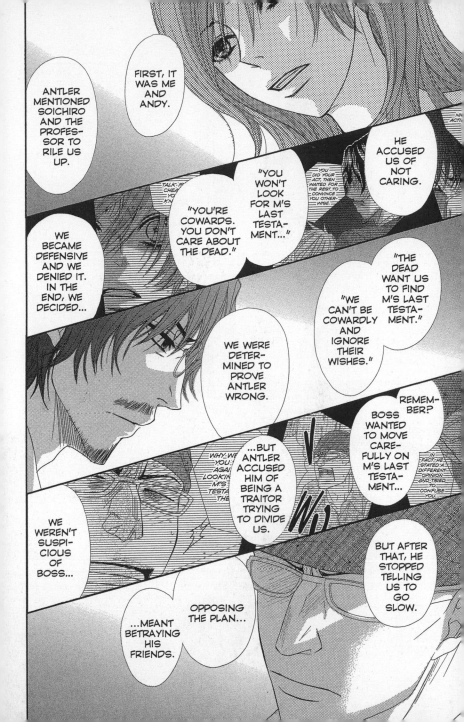

...WE COULDN'T TURN BACK.

THAT WAS THE PROBLEM.

BUT AFTER ANTLER CALLED...

ANDY AND I INSISTED ON SEARCHING EVEN THOUGH WE HAD A BIT OF DOUBT.

...ANTLER WANTED.

BOSS WAS UNSURE, BUT HE DECIDED NOT TO SAY ANYTHING. THAT'S EXACTLY WHAT...

WE COULD BE WRONG, AND NO ONE WOULD NOTICE UNTIL IT WAS TOO LATE.

THAT'S EXTREMELY DANGEROUS.

WE WERE ALL GOING IN THE SAME DIRECTION AND LEFT NO ROOM FOR QUESTIONING.

THAT WAY, HE COULD MANIPULATE OUR THOUGHTS AND ACTIONS.

ANTLER WANTED US TO GO OVER THAT LEDGE.

WE WERE HEADED IN THAT DIRECTION.

I WAS SCARED, BUT I DIDN'T KNOW WHY.

I'VE BEEN FEELING SO UNCERTAIN...

IS THIS WHAT WAS BOTHERING ME?

...

GASP

WASN'T IT THE SAME FOR YOU, BOSS? ANDY?

ONCE I REALIZED HIS TRICK, I FINALLY WOKE UP.

I'm trained in psychology, after all.

...BUT I'M PRETTY SURE.

I CAN'T PROVE IT...

ALL OF US FELT GUILTY THAT WE LET SOICHIRO AND THE PROFESSOR DIE.

ANTLER USED OUR WEAKNESS AGAINST US.

JUST LIKE WITH KUROSAKI.

Group hypnosis, huh?

NOW I FEEL EXCITED, LIKE JUSTICE IS ON OUR SIDE.

WE KEPT PUSHING OURSELVES, SAYING "WE CAN'T STOP" AND "IT'S OUR DECISION."

YES. I FELT A CHILL GO DOWN MY SPINE.

THAT'S WHY WE JUMPED AT THE CHANCE TO GET AHOLD OF M'S LAST TESTAMENT.

WE WERE DYING FOR A CHANCE TO EASE OUR GUILT.

DAMN, I'M EMBARRASSED...

BUT WE DIDN'T ADMIT IT.

WE JUST CONCENTRATED ON HELPING A KID WHO WAS A HANDFUL.

THE ONE WE THOUGHT NEEDED HELP ACTUALLY SAVED THIS TEAM.

BUT EVEN MORE THAN THAT, IT'S BECAUSE OF YOU, TERU.

HEH HEH...

HUH? WHY? I DIDN'T DO ANYTHING...

Actually, I don't understand what Kurosaki did either.

DID I MAKE YOU GUYS WORRY THAT MUCH?

NOW DON'T START ACTING LIKE YOU KNOW IT ALL.

TO BE HONEST, YES.

We'll go drinking soon.

You can pay.

HA HA HA... HE'S RIGHT.

BUT TASUKU...

YOU'RE THE ONE WHO DID IT.

HOW DO I PUT IT? YOU WERE OUR VOICE.

CHUCKLE

TERU, JUST STAY THE WAY YOU ARE.

?

NOW ...

WHAT TO DO FROM HERE ON OUT...

WE'LL CONTINUE WITH DECIPHERING THE CODE.

I'LL EXPLAIN TO TAKEDA THAT WE'RE CHANGING PLANS, THOUGH.

Good idea.

Yes.

Yes.

WE'LL ASK HIM TO BE FLEXIBLE.

THE AGENCY...

AS FOR US...

WE NEED TO FIGURE OUT WHY ANTLER TRIED TO USE US.

DON'T WORRY. LEAVE IT TO ME.

WSP

"Scrub Brush"...

BECAUSE THERE WAS SOMETHING ELSE THAT "SCRUB BRUSH" DIDN'T WANT US TO FIND!

I KNOW!

WHY DID HE WANT US TO CONCENTRATE SOLELY ON FINDING M'S LAST TESTAMENT?

THAT'S—

AND THAT GOES FOR AKIRA TOO.

PERHAPS THE REAL M'S LAST TESTAMENT IS SOMEWHERE ELSE.

RIGHT...

MAYBE IT'S TIME TO LOOK AT MY CELL PHONE!

...THAT THERE'S SOMETHING CRUCIAL NEARBY.

I HAVE A FEELING...

A TARGET FROM THE START... COVETED BY MANY!

YOU COULD BE RIGHT... ANTLER DOESN'T WANT US TO SEE SOMETHING.

GEE, THANKS.

TOK

YES, A SHAME. IT WAS ONLY INTERESTING BECAUSE OF DAISY'S MESSAGES.

And whaddaya mean "coveted"?

THAT CAN'T BE IT. I CHECKED IT OVER AND OVER AGAIN.

SHUT UP. DON'T BRING IT UP UNLESS YOU WANT ME TO DIE.

Sure, he would. Along with Chiharu.

I WONDER IF AKIRA READ THE DAISY MESSAGES TOO?

IF THERE WAS IMPORTANT DATA, AKIRA WOULD'VE FOUND IT.

THAT'S TRUE...

AKIRA TOOK THAT PHONE ONCE TOO, RIGHT?

At the amusement park.

VRRR

OH...

I HAVE IT ON VIBRATE.

OH, IT'S HARUKA.

VRR

Haruka

OH...!

Haruka

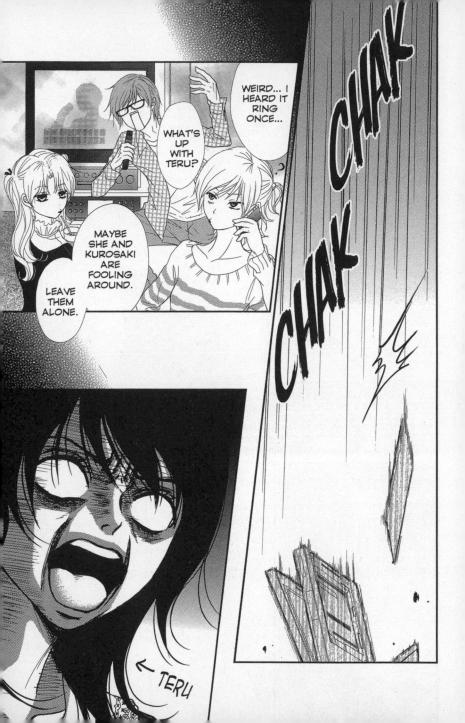

IT WAS MY ONLY MEMENTO FROM MY BROTHER...

Oh dear...

HEARTBREAK

OHHH...

MY BELOVED CELL PHONE...

AND IT HELD ALL THE BEAUTIFUL MEMORIES OF MY DEAR, GENTLE DAISY...

IT'S NOT BROKEN. THE COVER CAME OFF AND THE BATTERY FELL OUT, IS ALL.

I'm not gone. I'm right here.

He's gone forever...

CALM DOWN.

OKAY, HERE...

YEAH. HAND ME THAT COVER.

OH, REALLY?

Is that all?

SNAP☆

142

KAGAMIYAMA PRIVATE HIGH SCHOOL 1-7 (NUMBER 33) TERU KUREBAYASHI

OH, THAT ID INFO INSIDE THE COVER?

I SAW IT TOO, WHEN I ASKED THE AGENCY TO CHECK OUT YOUR PHONE.

...

WHAT IS THIS?

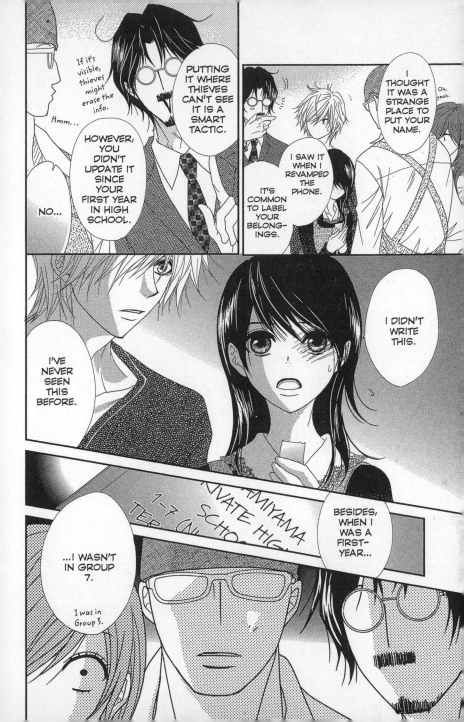

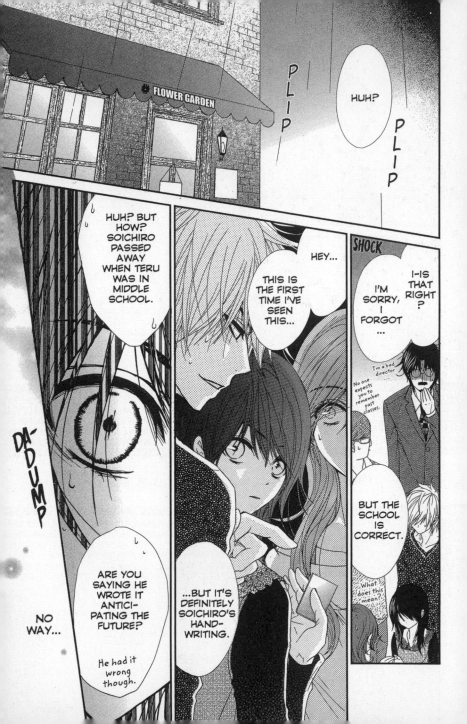

DID HE EVER VISIT THE SCHOOL WHILE HE WAS ALIVE?

BUT WHAT ABOUT SOICHIRO...?

I didn't know that, and I'm grateful...

YES. WE DISCUSSED YOUR SCHOOLING.

AS WELL AS HIRING KUROSAKI.

DIRECTOR...

DID MY BROTHER MENTION THE HIGH SCHOOL WHEN HE WAS ALIVE?

I LET HIM USE ONE OF THE EMPTY OFFICES.

HE CAME LOOKING FOR SOMEPLACE QUIET TO WORK ON THE CODE...

WELL...

WHY DO YOU ASK?

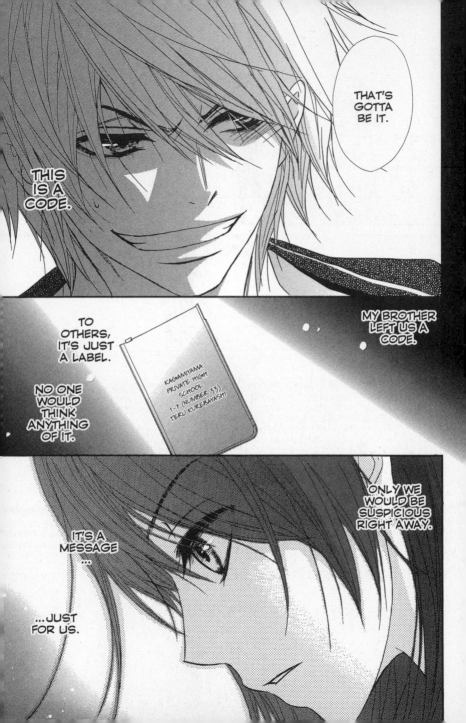

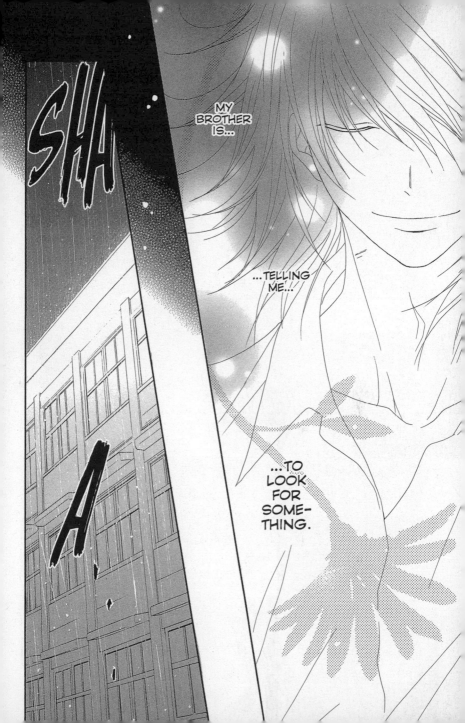

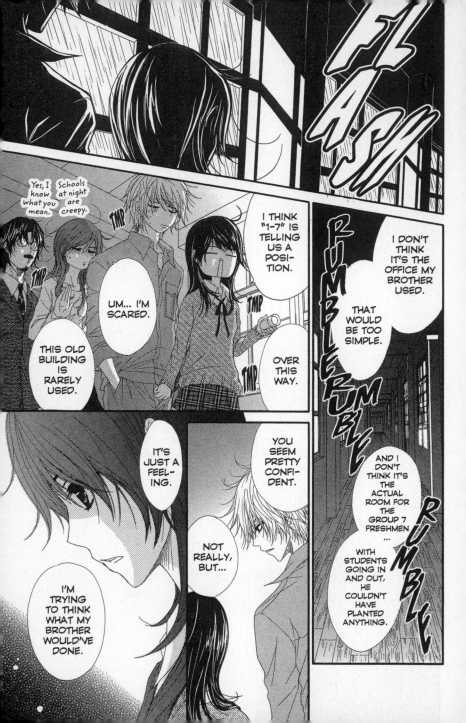

TMP

HERE WE ARE.

IT MUST BE HERE.

THIS IS THE SEVENTH ROOM ON THE FIRST FLOOR OF THE OLD BUILDING.

THIS ROOM ISN'T USED ANY-MORE...

IT'S THE OLD BIOLOGY REFER-ENCE ROOM.

REFERENCE ROOM (BIOLOGY)

ARE YOU READY?

I'M GOING TO OPEN THE DOOR.

I HAD A FEELING...

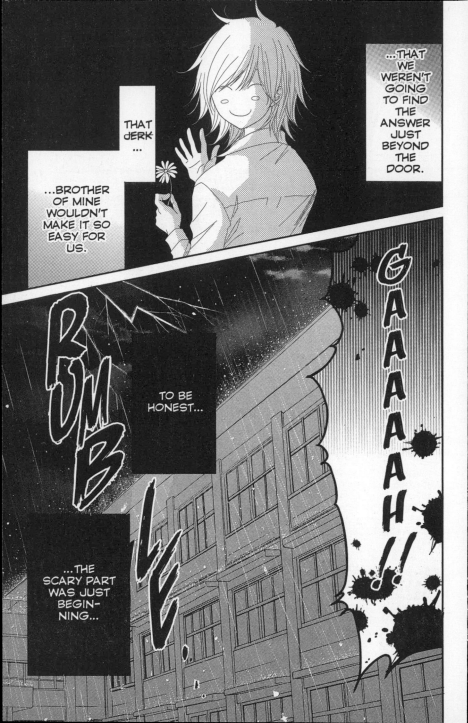

(RELOCATED) BALDLY ASK!!! ④

I'VE BEEN WONDERING SINCE VOLUME 1, BUT WHERE DOES TERU GET HER LIVING EXPENSES? SHE'S BEEN LIVING ALONE UNTIL RECENTLY, RIGHT? SHE HAS NO RELATIVES AND DOESN'T SEEM TO BE WORKING PART-TIME... MY GUESS IS THAT SHE 1) HAS HER BROTHER'S SAVINGS, 2) RECEIVES PUBLIC ASSISTANCE, OR 3) I SHOULDN'T WONDER ABOUT SUCH THINGS...LIKE WHY IN THE WORLD A GUY DRESSED IN BLACK WOULD RIDE A ROLLER COASTER BEFORE A BUSINESS DEAL. WOULD THE ANSWER FALL INTO ONE OF THESE THREE?

(IM, AICHI PREFECTURE)

HM... WHAT YOU'RE REFERRING TO WITH 3) HAS BEEN INVESTIGATED. (CO●N IS FUN, ISN'T IT?)

BUT YOU'RE RIGHT... YOU MUSTN'T KEEP PROBING EACH AND EVERY TIME, THE WAY KUROSAKI'S HAIRLINE KEEPS CHANGING IN EACH AND EVERY PANEL. BUT IN ANY CASE, THE CORRECT ANSWER IS 1) SOICHIRO'S SAVINGS. HE LEFT HER SOME MONEY, BUT IT WASN'T A HUGE AMOUNT. SO SHE THINKS OF THE FUTURE AND BUDGETS VERY CAREFULLY. IT'S NOT AS THOUGH SHE'S FORGOTTEN ABOUT LIVING FRUGALLY. REALLY! (DEFENSIVE)

IN VOLUME 5, RIKO, WHO WAS A BIT (?) UPSET AT KUROSAKI, CRUSHING A GLASS BOTTLE IN HER HAND. HOW STRONG IS HER GRIP ANYWAY? BY THE WAY, I'M 15 YEARS OLD AND I CAN DO 86 POUNDS. IT'S TRUE.

(GLOOMY, SHIZUOKA PREFECTURE)

EIGHTY-SIX POUNDS? WOW. THAT'S COOL. RIKO PROBABLY CAN SQUEEZE 66 POUNDS, WHICH IS AVERAGE FOR A WOMAN. ONLY WHEN SHE NEEDED TO TEACH KUROSAKI AND SOICHIRO A LESSON REGARDING SEXUAL HARASSMENT, THEN HER GRIP JUMPED TO LIKE 265 LBS. IT SEEMS SOICHIRO OFTEN WALKED A TIGHTROPE.

WHAT IS "GOBIIN"?

(SACHI, HIROSHIMA PREFECTURE)

IT'S THE SAME AS "GABIIN," WHICH IS A JAPANESE SOUND EFFECT THAT'S OFTEN USED IN OTHER MANGA. BUT I'M SUCH A NEWBIE, SO I HAVEN'T EARNED THE RIGHT TO USE A FAMOUS SOUND EFFECT LIKE THAT. THAT'S WHY I INNOVATED AND CAME UP WITH MY OWN. IT SOUNDS SORTA STUPID, BUT IT'S GOT CHARACTER AND I LIKE IT.

*THIS IS ANOTHER VARIATION. I'M SO GLAD THERE ARE READERS WHO ARE CHECKING.

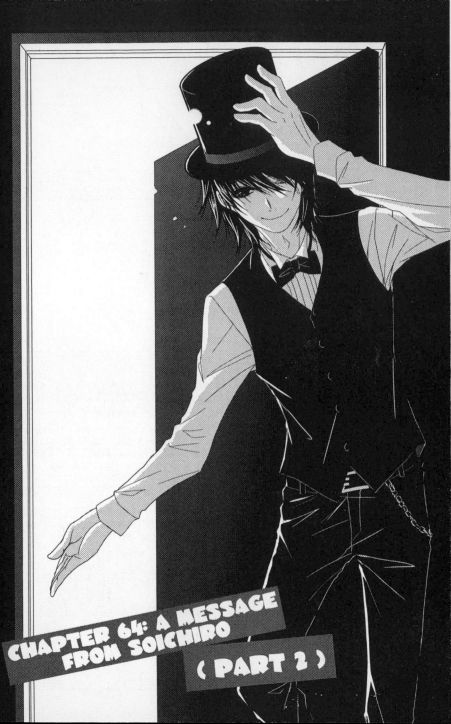

CHAPTER 64: A MESSAGE FROM SOICHIRO
(PART 2)

READY?

I'M OPENING THE DOOR.

KIYOSHI AND RENA APPEAR IN JUST ONE PANEL IN THIS VOLUME. HARUKA IS IN TWO. (KAKO IS IN ONE.)
IN VOLUMES 11 AND 12, THEY WERE ALL OVER THE PLACE AS IF THEY WERE THE MAIN CHARACTERS. SHOJO MANGA TENDS TO HAVE LOTS OF CHARACTERS, SO TRYING TO GIVE EVERYONE EQUAL TIME IS SUCH A BURDEN, THE STRESS COULD REACH LIFE-THREATENING LEVELS. PLEASE FORGIVE ME.

HEY! IF I'M NOT IN THE MANGA, THE RATIO OF GOOD-LOOKING GUYS WILL PLUMMET...!

WHAT ARE YOU SAYING? ARE YOU OUT OF YOUR MIND?

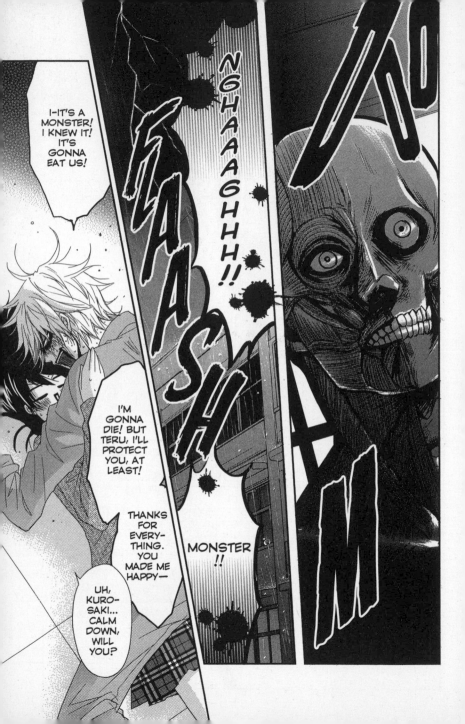

THIS IS A BIOLOGY REFERENCE ROOM, AFTER ALL.

Hmm... Yes...

LOOKS LIKE IT'S AN OLD ANATOMY MODEL?

DON'T BE SCARED, YOU GUYS.

WHICH MEANS, WE'D BETTER LOOK HARD.

THERE'S A CERTAIN MOOD HERE WITH THESE OLD SPECIMENS.

YES, *YOU* ESPECIALLY.

IT'S A GOOD PLACE TO HIDE SOMETHING, IF THAT'S WHAT SOICHIRO DID.

YOUR THEORY MIGHT BE RIGHT, TERU.

A SLIGHT BLOWUP, BUT NOT TO WORRY. JUST KEEP WATCH.

HEY, WHAT WAS ALL THAT SCREAMING JUST NOW?

Is there some kind of biohazard?

"BOSS IS GUARDING THE FRONT GATE (TO STOP ANYONE WHO TRIES TO INTERFERE)

HE LEFT A SECRET MESSAGE IN MY CELL PHONE...

THERE COULD BE SOME CLUES...

...EVEN THOUGH IT MAY NOT BE OBVIOUS.

MAYBE, JUST MAYBE, WE'LL FIND THE TRUTH BEHIND M'S LAST TESTAMENT.

KNOWING MY BROTHER...

...IT'S NOT GOING TO BE EASY.

WE WERE SEARCH- ING...

...FOR DATA LEFT BY MY BROTHER SOICHIRO.

KAGAMIYAMA PRIVATE HIGH SCHOOL (NUMBER 33) KUREBAYASHI

HERE'S WHAT PUZZLES ME THE MOST—

RIGHT... IT'S A BIG HINT FOR WHAT WE'RE LOOKING FOR.

WHAT DOES "NUMBER 33" MEAN?

Mumble Mumble **FWP FWP** Hmm...

THE FACTORS ARE 3 AND 11. MAYBE THEY'RE FILE NUMBERS IN HERE?

NO, HE WOULDN'T DO THE SAME THING TWICE.

COULD IT BE A POSITION MARKER LIKE "1-7"?

LIKE THREE TO THE LEFT, THREE TO THE RIGHT?

I THINK IT'S A BINARY NUMBER. 33 IS 100001... IN A FILING SYSTEM, MAYBE?

TAKE THE TWO END NUMBERS, THEN THE NUMBERS IN BETWEEN.

SOICHIRO WAS A GENIUS. LEAVE IT TO HIM TO DO THE UNEXPECTED.

TERU? WHAT'S THE MATTER?

THE NUMBER 33... REMINDS ME OF EARS.

THAT'S CRAZY! SOICHIRO WOULDN'T BE SO STUPID!

HUH?! WHAT ARE YOU DOING?!

PU SH

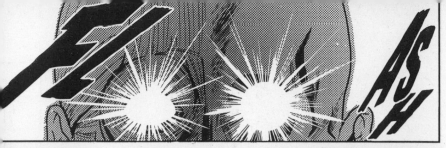
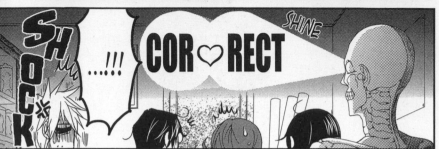
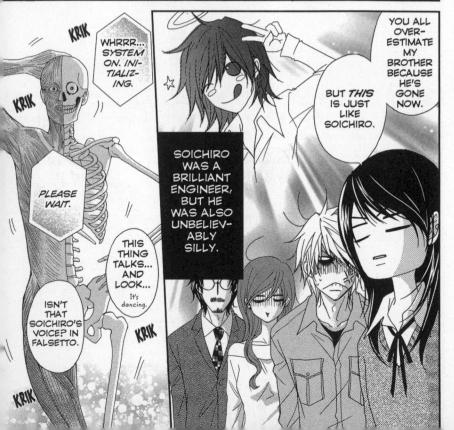

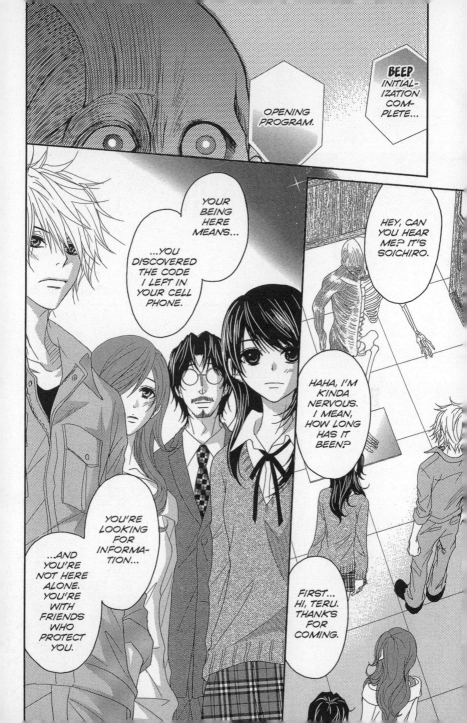

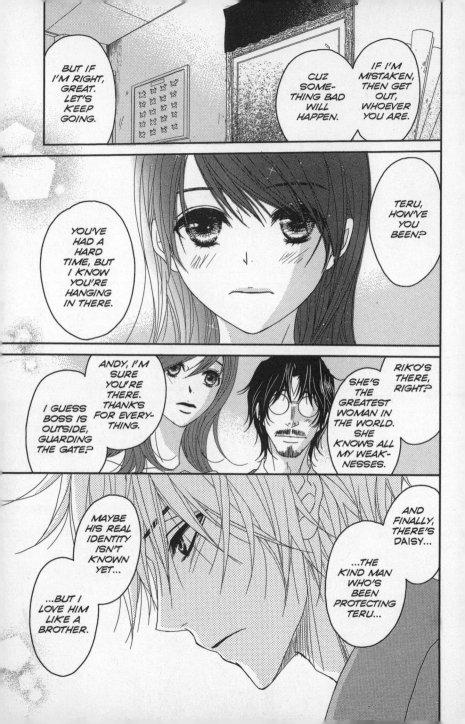

KRIK KRIK KRIK KRIK

C'MON. GIVE ME A HUG.

NOW, NOW... IT'S OKAY TO CRY.

...BUT HEARING HIS VOICE COMING THROUGH A SKELETON IS...

THIS IS SUPPOSED TO BE A TOUCHING REUNION...

I know.

OUR HIGH ESTEEM IS FALLING RATHER QUICKLY.

HE'S SUCH A FOOL, EVEN IN DEATH.

Well, I'm not surprised.

Oh, he expected our reaction.

YOU'RE PROBABLY CALLING ME NAMES BY NOW, SO I'LL GET TO THE POINT.

ANYWAY...

LET ME ASK EACH ONE OF YOU NOW...

THIS "MYSTERY"...

ARE YOU PREPARED TO FOLLOW IT UNTIL THE END?

IG-NORE THAT, TERU. IT'S DAISY. DAISY.

...TASU-KU— I MEAN, DAISY.

Oops...

I'M GONNA PULVE-RIZE YOU.

KRIK KRIK

TERU...

RIKO, ANDY...

BOSS AND...

WELL, THIS IS YOUR LAST CHANCE TO TURN BACK. THINK HARD.

IT COULD BE MORE THAN YOU BARGAINED FOR.

MAYBE YOU'RE ALREADY DEEPLY INVOLVED?

IN THIS BATTLE, A HAPPY ENDING ISN'T GUARAN- TEED.

...YOU'LL HAVE TO SHOULDER A HEAVY BURDEN.

IF YOU DECIDE TO KEEP GOING...

ARE YOU PREPARED FOR THAT?

I'LL TAKE YOUR SILENCE AS A "YES."

OKAY THEN.

COR- RECT.

PRESS THE CUTEST PART OF ME.

TERU...

PRESS

BELLY BUTTON

HAH?!

WHAT THE—?! A TRAP DOOR?! This isn't a ninja castle!!

...I PUT IN A LITTLE CONTRAPTION.

"LITTLE" CONTRAPTION? LIKE HELL IT IS!

VRRRRR

TO TEST YOUR RESOLVE...

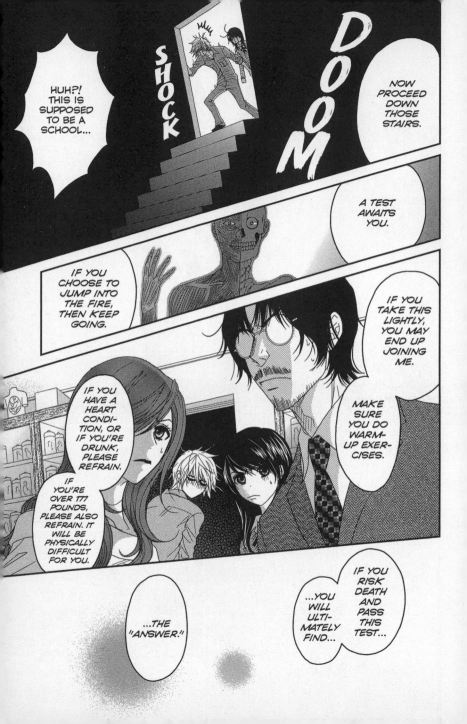

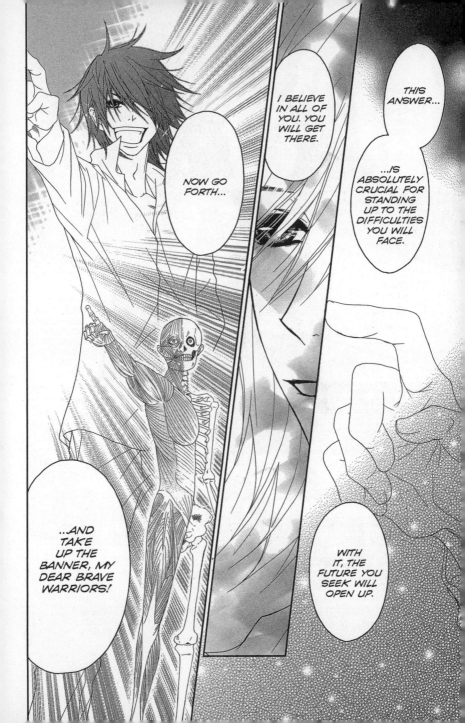

YOUR DOCTORED CELL PHONE IS COMING IN HANDY, TERU.

WATCH YOUR STEP, EVERYONE.

TMP
TMP

DON'T GIVE MY BROTHER SO MUCH LEEWAY. HE'LL JUST TAKE ADVANTAGE OF IT.

THAT WAS A BIG HINT, RIGHT?

WHAT WAS THAT ABOUT "DEAR BRAVE WARRIORS"?

YUP... HE'S DEAD AND IT'S GOTTEN EVEN WORSE.

TMP
TMP

TERU, GET BEHIND ME. I'LL HOLD THE LIGHT.

This looks scary. We should call Boss.

Can't. He weighs over 177 lbs.

OH, THAT'S OKAY.

LISTEN TO ME.

THIS USED TO BE THE OLD ARMY'S SPECIAL WHO-KNOWS-WHAT.

WAS THIS CONSTRUCTION APPROVED?

HENCE, THE WEIRD DEVICES I'VE TRIED SOME.

That's why things keep popping up all over the place.

It's an underground passage.

SH-SHUT UP! IT'S NOT LIKE THAT!

THERE'S NO TELLING WHAT'LL SPRING UP NEXT.

SO DEFEN- SIVE...

HMM... TRYING TO EARN POINTS ALREADY.

STAY CLOSE. I'LL PROTECT YOU.

HA HA... BUT THIS IS JUST THE BEGIN- NING...

KLIK

IT'S SO- ICHIRO. HE WON'T GO EASY ON US!

THEN YOU GUYS BETTER WATCH OUT TOO.

THEN AGAIN, NO TELLING WHEN SOICHIRO WILL PASS JUDG- MENT.

ANDY!!

SHO

GAH

!!!......!!

WHOOSH

HEEEEY!

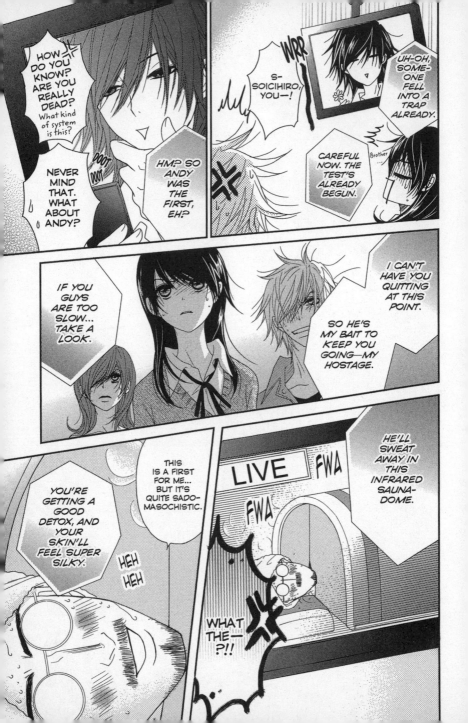

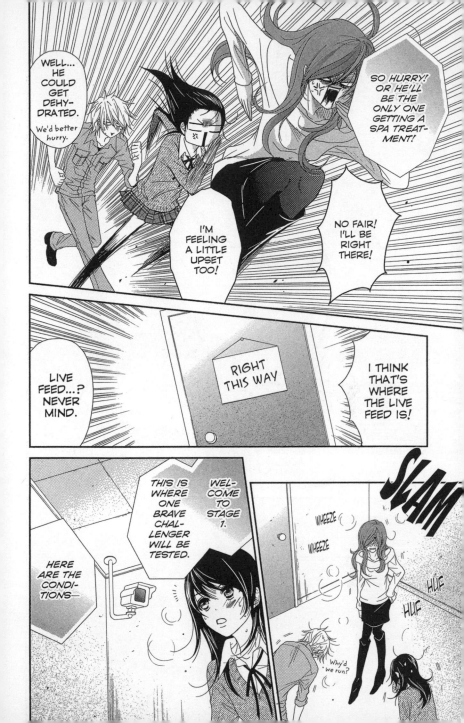

I'm 5'5" and a D-cup, incidentally.

FINE, I'LL DO IT.

HMPH... I GUESS HE'S ASKING SPECIFI-CALLY FOR ME.

SOMEONE HEALTHY AND FIT AND ABLE TO MAKE CALM, SMART DECI-SIONS.

YOUNG FEMALE. MUST BE OVER 5'3" WITH BOOBS BIGGER THAN A C-CUP.

Um... You're an A...

Darn... I don't have the height.

I SAID "YOUNG" FEMALE.

How is he able to carry on a conversation?

NOT AT ALL. MISTRESS RIKO IS PERFECTLY FINE.

CRACK CRACK

IS THAT A COMPLAINT? DO YOU WANT TO DIE A SECOND TIME?

GOOD LUCK! SEE YOU!

RIKO, DO YOUR STUFF.

Don't get reckless.

ALTHOUGH HOW WELL RIKO DOES HERE COULD AFFECT YOUR PROGRESS.

THE REMAIN-ING MEMBERS SHOULD GET GOING NOW.

S L A M

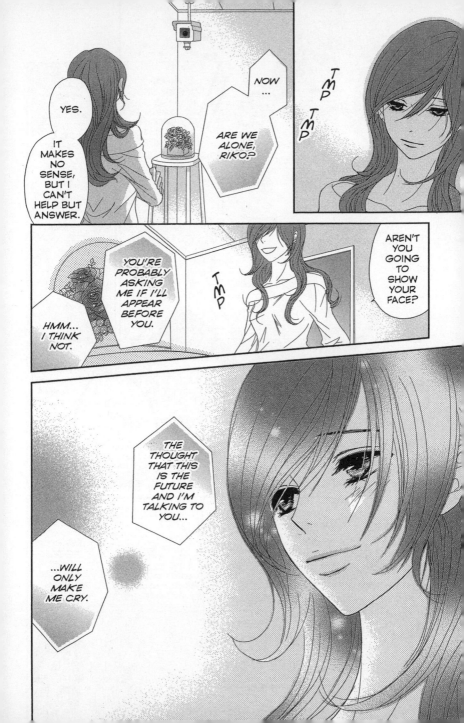

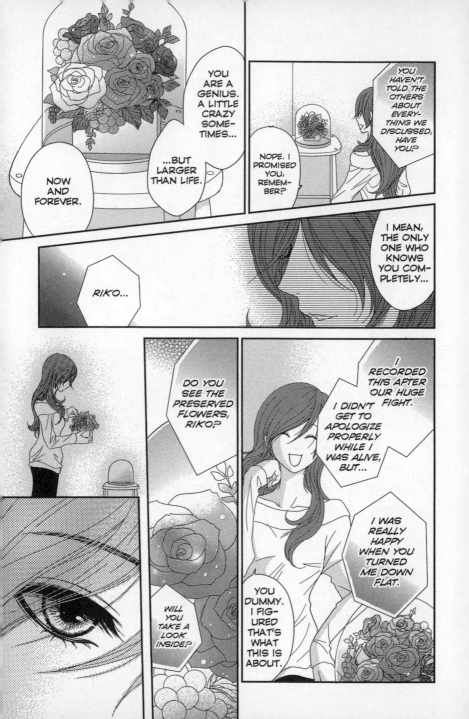

YOU'RE DOING THIS NOW?

I'M SORRY ABOUT THE TIME AND PLACE.

ANY-WAY... THAT'S ALL, RIKO.

PLEASE GO AFTER TERU AND TASUKU.

MAYBE YOU'RE READY TO DECIDE NOW...

...OR YOU CAN EXCHANGE IT AND GET BBQ MEAT INSTEAD.

STILL SAYING SUCH THINGS... IDIOT...

HUH? THAT'S IT? NO TEST?

TMP

TMP

TMP

ACTUALLY, I WANTED YOU TO DO A PINK LADY* NUMBER OR SOME-THING...

BUT I WON'T BE ABLE TO SEE YOU ANYWAY...

*A popular singing duo of the late '70s and early '80s

OH, SORRY. I WASN'T LISTENING... I WAS THINKING ABOUT SOMETHING.

WHAT?

I DOUBT SOICHIRO WILL PUT RIKO THROUGH THE WRINGER.

IF ANYTHING, HE'LL TELL HER TO DO A PINK LADY DANCE...

HM?

TMP TMP

TMP

TERU, ARE YOU WORRIED ABOUT RIKO?

SOICHIRO SAID THE ANSWER LIES AHEAD...

...BUT MAYBE SOMEONE ALREADY TOOK IT.

WELL...

THE PUZZLES HAVEN'T BEEN THAT HARD UP 'TIL NOW...

I DON'T THINK OTHERS COULD'VE FIGURED THEM OUT.

I FIGURED OUT THE LABEL...

...BUT OTHERS COULD'VE TOO.

MY CELL PHONE WAS TAKEN SEVERAL TIMES.

WE MAY NOT BE THE FIRST ONES HERE.

WHAT DO YOU MEAN?

The code is...

Like the ears... and the belly button.

Someone in the school may've found it...

There's Akira and Chiharu.

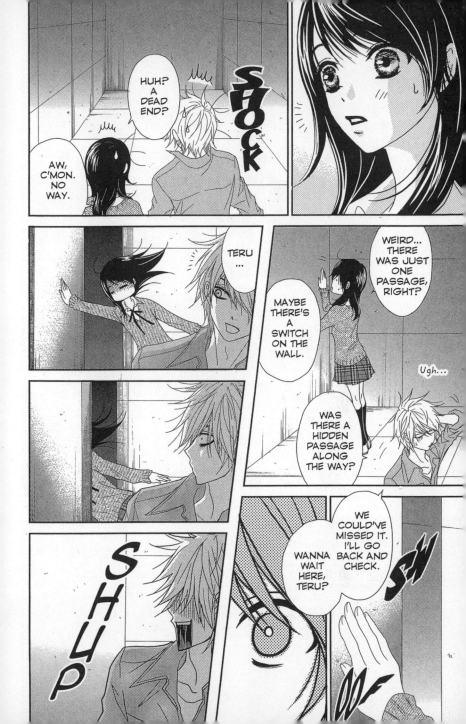

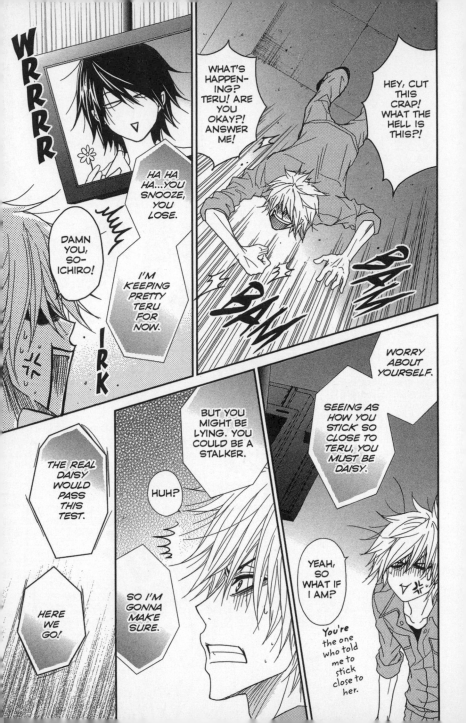

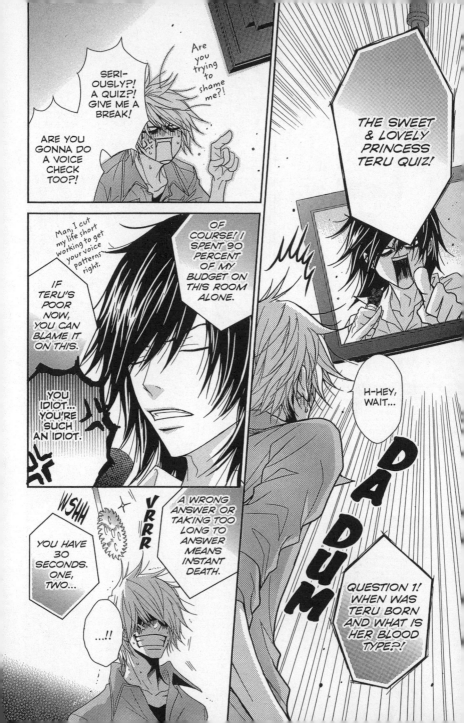

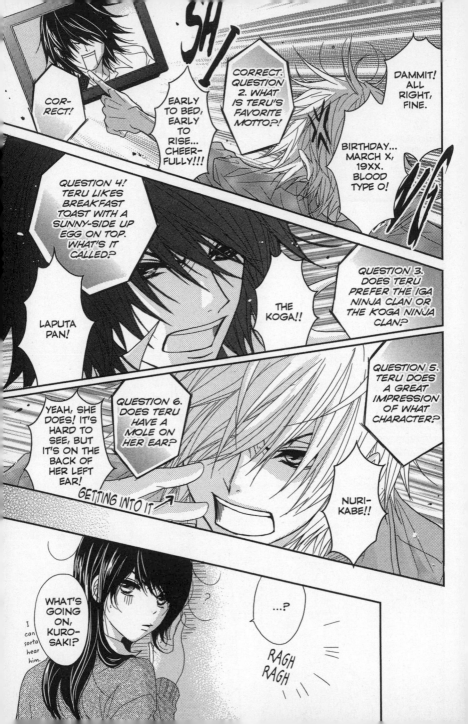

YEAH, RIGHT. YOU PROBABLY DID SOMETHING TO IT.

Although it's canned to prevent spoilage.

SO RELAX AND HAVE A SNACK.

MACKEREL

DON'T WORRY, MY HONEY. THEY'RE HAVING FUN ON THE OTHER SIDE.

AM I GOING TO BE TESTED TOO?

SO?

ACTUALLY, TERU... THERE'S NOTHING FOR YOU.

HA HA... SORRY.

I PASSED ON EVERYTHING I WANTED YOU TO LEARN WHEN I WAS ALIVE. I'M SO PROUD OF YOU, LITTLE SISTER.

I KNOW YOU WILL BE HAPPY.

WAIT HERE JUST A WHILE LONGER.

HE'LL BE FINISHED REAL SOON.

THAT WAS FAST. CORRECT, BUT YOU GET DEATH...

THAT'S WHAT YOU DESERVE, BUT I FORGIVE YOU. I ALWAYS KNEW YOU AND I WERE ALIKE.

But restrain yourself, huh?

Oops...

S-SORRY...

QUESTION 98. WHAT'S HER COLOR PREFERENCE FOR UNDERWEAR?

QUESTION 96! WHEN TERU GAINS WEIGHT, WHERE DOES SHE PUT ON THE POUNDS?

HER INNER THIGHS! HER BOOBS WILL NEVER GET BIG!

GOT IT!

QUESTION 97. WHAT SONG DOES TERU OFTEN SING IN THE BATH?

"YOSA-KU."

NOW FOR QUESTION 99.

TOO EASY! WHITE!!

DOES TERU...

...KNOW YOUR TRUE IDENTITY...

...AND THE TRUTH BEHIND YOUR SIN?

THEN HERE IS THE FINAL QUESTION. NUMBER 100...

I SEE. OKAY.

SHE'S KNOWN FOR A LONG TIME.

YEAH.

I TOLD YOU TO SUFFER. I WOULDN'T LET YOU FORGET YOUR SIN.

THIS IS JUST A PROGRAM.

DO YOU RESENT ME FOR THAT?

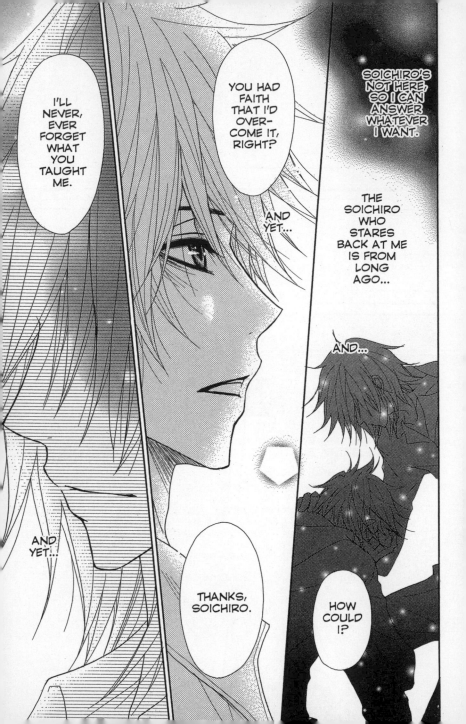

CONGRATS, DAISY. YOU PASS.

HMM... GOOD.

Oh, we caught up with them!

THANKS FOR MAKING IT HERE.

PLEASE CONTINUE TO TAKE CARE OF TERU.

THANKS TO THE REST OF YOU TOO.

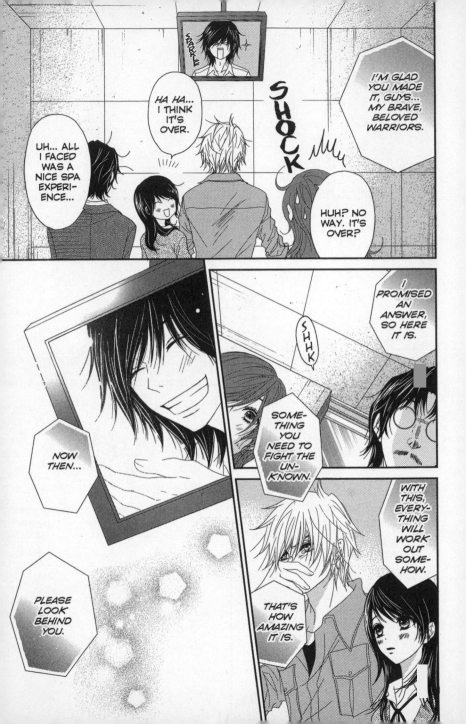

THE END

Our friends are what's important.

OH, I SEE. SO THIS IS THE ANSWER ...

I FIGURED THAT OUT MIDWAY THOUGH.

TOO BAD BOSS WASN'T HERE THEN.

He's never here when it's important.

That's for sure.

THAT'S OKAY. THIS WAS *SO* SOICHIRO. ANYWAY, IT WAS FUN.

TEAM KURE-BAYASHI IS DONE!

SORRY ABOUT MY BROTHER, EVERYONE ...

ONE THING'S FOR SURE...

It was in the spa room addressed to Boss.

OH, KUROSAKI, DON'T FORGET THE FREEBIE.

I think it's an old bottle of wine.

What's in that box, Andy?

I WON'T.

NO ONE OTHER THAN US WOULD HAVE EVER MADE IT.

FREEBIE

PROFESSOR M'S HDD WITH DATA DECIPHERED, CRUCIAL INFORMATION RELATED TO M AND OTHER THINGS.

WE'RE TAKING ALL THIS WITH US...

IF YOU NEED THIS, BE SURE TO TAKE IT WITH YOU. HANDLE WITH CARE.

...SO-ICHIRO.

DENGEKI DAISY 13 *THE END*

THE BEST ☆ OF ☆ THE SECRET SCHOOL CUSTODIAN OFFICE ♥

THERE IS A *DENGEKI DAISY* FAN SEGMENT BOLDLY FEATURED IN *BETSUCOMI* THAT IS APTLY TITLED, "THE SECRET SCHOOL CUSTODIAN OFFICE♥"!

WITH ARBITRARY EYES, WE EXAMINED ALL THE GREAT WORK FEATURED THERE AND PICKED THE "BEST" AMONG THEM THAT WE WANTED TO LEAVE FOR POSTERITY!

THE "BEST OF" FOR VOLUME 13 IS... "WINNERS OF THE CAPTIONING CONTEST"

YOUR WILD IDEAS DAZZLED US! WE SELECTED THE STRONGEST ENTRIES FROM THE MANY, MANY POST-CARDS WE RECEIVED AND PRESENT THEM HERE!!

DENGEKI DAISY CAPTION-ING CONTEST WINNERS!!

WHAT KUROSAKI SAID IN RESPONSE TO THE EXPRESSION ON TERU'S FACE?!

SHE USUALLY EATS NATTO BEANS OR YOGURT FOR BREAKFAST...

❶ THERE'S NATTO...

❷ ...ON YOUR FACE.

–NATTO LADY, YAMAGATA PREFECTURE

MERRY CHRIST-MAS

❶ WOOLEN PANTIES...

❷ ...HAVE GOT TO BE RED.

–MIYUCCHI, HIROSHIMA PREFECTURE

I WAS TRYING TO LOOK KISSABLE...

❶ UPON CLOSER INSPECTION...

❷ ...YOUR LIPS ARE REALLY POINTY.

–HINA, KAGAWA PREFECTURE

S H O C K

❶ THERE'S SEAWEED ON YOUR TEETH.

❷ THERE'S A WIG ON YOUR HEAD!

GREEN SEAWEED   WIG

–PONZU, NAGASAKI PREFECTURE

NO.1 FIRST PRIZE
WINS AN AUTOGRAPH!

❶ YOU...

❷ ...HAVE A PRETTY CROOKED CHIN.

–ZUCCHI, YAMAGUCHI PREFECTURE

I'LL PROTECT YOUR CHIN TOO!!

JUDGES' COMMENTS

■ THE READERS' LINES ARE CLASSIC AND SO ARE THE INTERJECTIONS BY EDITOR ITO. I MEAN, COME ON. "MERRY CHRISTMAS"?! (THIS IS PRAISE.)
(HEAD JUDGE: KYOUSUKE MOTOMI SENSEI!)

■ TELLING TERU THAT SHE'S GOT A CROOKED CHIN SEEMS TO BE AN EXCUSE TO TOUCH HER...AND IT'S A LOVABLE SIDE OF KUROSAKI THAT WAS CAPTURED BEAUTIFULLY.
(JUDGE: *DAISY* EDITOR)

BETSUCOMI, THE MAGAZINE THAT SERIALIZES *DAISY*, GOES ON SALE EVERY MONTH AROUND THE 13TH! PLEASE LOOK FOR IT IF YOU WANT TO READ "THE SECRET SCHOOL CUSTODIAN OFFICE"! ♥

AFTERWORD

OKAY!!! THIS IS THE END OF *DENGEKI DAISY* VOLUME 13.

WHAT DO YOU THINK? IT'S BEEN GETTING PRETTY COMPLICATED IN *DAISY*, AND I'VE PACKED QUITE A LOT OF STUFF IN THIS VOLUME. ARE THINGS COMING TO A HEAD OR NOT...? IN ANY CASE, I'D BE SO HAPPY IF YOU CONTINUE TO FOLLOW THE STORY. I'M GOING TO DO MY VERY BEST TO KEEP GOING AT FULL STEAM. SO I'LL SEE YOU AGAIN!!

KYOUSUKE MOTOMI

最富キョウスケ

DENGEKI DAISY
C/O VIZ MEDIA
P.O. BOX 77010
SAN FRANCISCO, CA
94107

IF YOU HAVE ANY QUESTIONS, PLEASE
← SEND THEM HERE. FOR REGULAR
FAN MAIL, PLEASE SEND THEM TO THE
SAME ADDRESS BUT CHANGE THE
ADDRESSEE TO:

KYOUSUKE MOTOMI
C/O DENGEKI DAISY
EDITOR

...AND THAT'S IT. THANK YOU VERY MUCH!!

Lately, when I hit a wall with the storyboard, I go into my kitchen and start cleaning. There are lots of products on the market like Sesquicarbonate Soda, as well as regular sodium bicarbonate, and I'm steadily improving my cleaning skills. But I still have a hard time with my storyboard. It's tough!

-Kyousuke Motomi

Born on August 1, Kyousuke Motomi debuted in *Deluxe Betsucomi* with *Hetakuso Kyupiddo* (No-Good Cupid) in 2002. She is the creator of *Otokomae! Biizu Kurabu* (Handsome! Beads Club), and her latest work, *Dengeki Daisy*, is currently being serialized in *Betsucomi*. Motomi enjoys sleeping, tea ceremonies and reading Haruki Murakami.

DENGEKI DAISY
VOL. 13
Shojo Beat Edition

STORY AND ART BY
KYOUSUKE MOTOMI

DENGEKI DAISY Vol.13
by Kyousuke MOTOMI
© 2007 Kyousuke MOTOMI
All rights reserved.
Original Japanese edition published by SHOGAKUKAN.
English translation rights in the United States of America
and Canada arranged with SHOGAKUKAN.

Translation & Adaptation/JN Productions
Touch-up Art & Lettering/Rina Mapa
Design/Nozomi Akashi
Editor/Amy Yu

The stories, characters and incidents mentioned in this
publication are entirely fictional.

No portion of this book may be reproduced or transmitted
in any form or by any means without written permission
from the copyright holders.

Printed in the U.S.A.

Published by VIZ Media, LLC
P.O. Box 77010
San Francisco, CA 94107

10 9 8 7 6 5 4 3 2 1
First printing, December 2013

www.viz.com

www.shojobeat.com

PARENTAL ADVISORY
DENGEKI DAISY is rated T+ for Older Teen and is
recommended for ages 16 and up. This volume contains
suggestive themes.
ratings.viz.com

This is the last page.

In keeping with the original Japanese comic format, this book reads from right to left—so action, sound effects, and word balloons are completely reversed. This preserves the orientation of the original artwork—plus, it's fun! Check out the diagram shown here to get the hang of things, and then turn to the other side of the book to get started!